BEEF EVER

G000123078

Kevin Newman has the same birthday as James Bernard Clifton, also went to school in Brighton and Hove and (like him) both left, and returned to, his home county of Sussex. There the similarities end, however – Kevin is a prolific author of books, articles and newspaper supplements but this is his first published novel. He is a bit of a teacher, a bit of a Sussex tour guide, and most of all, a bit chuffed that this unusual tale has finally been published. He is married with two boys, neither of whom have thankfully had a maths book thrown at their heads...

Beef Every Day, But No Latin

The story of a school started by a schoolboy

As told to

Kevin Newman

THE REAL PRESS

www.therealpress.co.uk

Published in 2020 by the Real Press.
www.therealpress.co.uk
© Kevin Newman

ISBN (print) 978-1912119219
ISBN (ebooks) 978-1912119202

To Patrick Fergus Brendan Newman – another (slightly later) Irish addition to Brighton and Hove, who also brought much to the city.

Contents & timetable

Lesson 1
Physics and Mathematics (propulsion, trajectories, angles and velocity)

Hove, 1925 and 1940

Living by the sea does strange things to a person, and even stranger ones to a boy.

There is something that can induce madness when half of your being is surrounded by somewhere wet, increasingly deep, dark and dangerous. The reduction of half of your travel options means one cannot always move where you physically want to and so the journeying you need becomes journeying of the mind.

Books in other words. I have heard it said that everyone has one book that will change their lives and take them somewhere. In my case, James Bernard McCarthy Clifton (that's Bernard to you, or Clifton as I was known back then), I'd have to agree that is true. I had a book once that took me down a very unusual road.

It wasn't, however a book I read. It was one that was thrown at me.

Thrown at my head to be precise. If you want to know that sort of detail. A copy of the snappily-titled *Advanced arithmetic and elementary algebra and mensuration, a text-book for secondary schools and students preparing for public examinations* was thrown across the classroom on a sunny May day in 1925. It was lobbed by my then crippled schoolmaster; the one-and-only Irish rogue, tippler (and lobber of books at schoolboys in a rare-old dilly-dreamworld), Mr Michael O'Byrne.

Mick, or MOB, as he was known for short, looked like your typical schoolmaster of that time. He was tall, broad-shouldered with sometimes tamed wild and wandering hair and a tailfin moustache. He was usually a lousy shot, due to his vision sometimes being a bit shaky from his time in the trenches, his penchant for Guinness before morning choir practice. But most of all this keen cricketer was a lousy shot as he didn't really want to make the book engage with your head (except in an educational sense).

He normally hurled a copy of Hardy at you so that it would land with a ruddy-great 'Whumph!' on your desk and 'scare the bejesus out of you', as he liked to put it.

But that wasn't to be the case this time. Either the Black Stuff (Guinness) or the Brown Stuff (whiskey) had gone down too easily (more than likely) that day, but the great big bulk of a book, 394-pages worth of the dullest tasks known to man or beast on God's good Earth, resplendent in a bulky hardback cover whacked me sideways on the head as I was looking down onto Holland Road out of the window.

One moment I was watching the good folk of Hove go about their daily business, with an air of purpose

2

that Sussex folk seem to hold, and the next thing I knew my brain had been sent an almighty wallop across my cranium, my skull seemed to throb and my teeth had made what seemed like their own separate journey across my mouth. The bottom of my jaw, I remember moved at a different pace from the top half and a gurgling "warragahh!" sound resonatedafrom my throat.

"Clifton!" shouted MOB. "Yer great pappy-headed mutton chop! What on earth are you dreaming about?"

And that, dearest reader, was this: I initially thought that I had been thinking about nothing at all, absolutely damn-all. Not home, not about mother; certainly not about father (which was rare), nor friends or even the good denizens of the town of Hove whom I had been staring at.

"Yer should be concentrating on yer studies, Clifton. This is no time to be lookin' at the women, so it isn't. Leave all that love and lust and thoughts of the women until you've a beard and nuts that reach the floor."

At this point, I should point out that MOB wasn't your usual schoolmaster. Despite his well-to-do background from a middling Irish family in Leighlinbridge, County Carlow, no delicacies of thought or expression were needed in his view. Nor, according to him, should young gentlemen be excused the odd fist or the language of the dockyard, the public bar or the factory.

Rationing of the coarse, the guttural, the offensive

3

and the malodorous phrase or word were seldom required, except when the Headmaster, Mr Chubb, slid into view (yes, that really was his name). MOB would insult, tease, insinuate and pester the living daylights out of you and tell you how much he detested you and 'every other frisky eleven-year-old' in that class. We weren't all actually eleven, but that hadn't seemed to have sunk in with MOB. To him, everyone was eleven years old and 'vermin', 'effluent', 'toe rags' and, usually by Friday, 'unwholesome scum'.

And we loved him for it. For even with his slight reek of Guinness farts and tobacco, the odd punch, his inability to remember your name by the afternoon, and to refer to each of us boys as 'You there!', for his ill-fitting gowns and failure to shave around his pronounced Adam's apple, there was something the other masters didn't have. Especially the insipid and aptly named headmaster, Mr Clovis Chubb, who needed the help of his mother to run Holland Road School.

MOB was a war hero, who in a previous life as Lieutenant M. O'Byrne of the London Regiment had taken a German bullet in his knee at Third Ypres in 1917, as he frequently told us. Despite mood swings, as a result of the pain he still suffered, he had a genuine warmth and sparkiness about him. He seemed in his own way to care for us; who we were, where we were going and who we were going to be one day. He might clip us around the heads (what teacher at that time didn't? This was a generation who had seen a millennium's worth of violence in a handful of years), but he would also rip out the fly leaves from books on which he would draw intricate pictures to give as prizes.

He would also make models for us of First World War aircraft and explain their workings. He was a fascinating mix of violence and gentleness and when Chubb was out we enjoyed his secret missions where he would send the fastest runners on to his 'Grog shop' in Church Street to purchase his copious amounts of cigarettes. His love of cricket pervaded every maths lesson and we were tricked into learning algebra, trigonometry, calculus and the dullest of dull equations by discussing the latest cricket match at the nearby County Cricket ground, which was also in Hove.

Holland House School had a deal with the Cricket Ground in neighbouring Palmeira Avenue, so we could use its grounds when Sussex weren't at play. This would come in handy for my school later on, after my breakaway from the Republic of Chubb and Mumsy Chubb.

And yes, I do mean *my* school. I started a school.

Events such as the looming General Strike, the chaos in Germany two years prior, politics, culture, arts, history and literature all came alive in the world of MOB. His engineering background before the war also meant he could apply the dullest bit of maths to a practical application. Of course, it was still a mathematics lesson, but to Michael O'Byrne there were no boundaries, no limits to what your ambitions should be and, on that wet Wednesday back in 1925, no reason why I should be staring out of the window. The cricket wasn't on or visible from there. So he chucked a book at me. Fair play.

The class laughed, especially as the shot had been such a prime one and the attached comments about my burgeoning libido and its aim at the good women at Hove scored a straight six. But then MOB's question hit me.

What had I been thinking about?

There must have been something going on in my Puny Mental Muscle for thought, or my PMM as I called my brain. And then it struck me. I *had* been thinking. I'd been contemplating what it would be like if *I* ran the school, and not Chubb. 'That great Mammy's Boy' we'd heard MOB call the Headmaster when he thought we weren't listening. For Chubb had assembled the most inept collection of practitioners of pedagogy ever possible that a boy's family could pay for. Apart from the Jewish science teacher, Pearl, only MOB had anything going for him.

As for our Latin master, I won't even begin to regale you with how one teacher could make a dead language want you to join it. Admittedly, in the decade after the Great War, masters were thin on the ground, along with menfolk as a whole, and many of the men who hadn't been left behind in the Flanders mud or the sand of the Dardanelles had left their mental faculties back there in the theatre of combat. If you had a pulse and could vaguely face the right way the teaching profession beckoned. Still, Chubb's men were a rum old bunch and I had been thinking, why don't those who schools are for – children, in other words, in case you're wondering, why don't *they* get to run them? Why is the responsibility for moulding of minds left to those who minds are the mouldiest?

In my life I've achieved a lot since that wet Wednesday. I've designed motion picture cameras, a bomb blast pressure recorder, and a mine detector to name just a few. That thought back in May 1925 that MOB had whacked into my brain didn't manage to go away though, and the result was that I indeed set up my own school, even as a mere 'frisky 11-year old'.

I too, as I said, became a Clovis Chubb of sorts (but without the Mother thankfully looming large) and that school? Well, it's still going today despite the war since you're asking (and I'm sure you were). In fact, that's where I'm heading now, despite being in the fullest reaches of adulthood, but first I need to pay MOB a visit too and see what he makes of this latest war. Amongst other things. If you want to join me and find out how it all came about, you're more than welcome.

I will warn you though, we will encounter one-legged Hollywood heartthrobs, savage mutts, a steely matron and I'll need to tell you all this hopefully without Hitler's Luftwaffe dropping bombs on us. There will also be generous amounts of beef. Thick, sinewy, gelatinous and tough chunks of the rotting carcasses of dead animals, which some people enjoy stuffing down their gullets.

If that doesn't sound too arduous, then do, by all means, tag along. Even in a busy town like Hove, with people all around, one can still be glad of the company. Life can be lonely at times, so do join me.

Speaking of Hove, I'd better tell you something of this place that dominated my formative years. Rather than now in September 1940 or even my early days in 1925 though, I'd better take you back before the Norman conquest.

Lesson 2
History (Local, Social, Economic)

Hove, 1940.

It's funny walking down these same streets again after so many years. Hove is a funny old town, for those of you that don't know it. It was apparently named by the Vikings, which explains its distinctive name amongst a sea of good Saxon place names and has been referred to over the years as Hova, Hoove and today Hove, which rhymes with 'grove', and said as in 'the ship hove into sight.'

It's definitely not Brighton. St Leonards is the grander end of Hastings and West Worthing the more genteel area of Worthing, but they're still an integral part of the other. Hove is just Hove. People say Brighton is London-By-The-Sea, but they're wrong. Hove has the grander architecture, the wider streets and the feel of the capital *au bord dela mer*. Hove is flat, like most of London, Brighton has the slums of the East End but hills you only get in London's surrounding villages.

It was once just a small fishing hamlet with one street, even appearing in the Domesday Books (there were actually two books, MOB always said) until the neighbouring landed family, the Stanfords, decided to sell off their land at the back of neighbouring Brighton and that encouraged development westerly towards Hove. The family were even called the Westerns at that time, a bit like the movies one gets at the cinema with cowboys in, and so the road that joined the two towns is today called Western Road. Lucky really, as it heads west from Brighton. If their family name had been the Southerns or even the Clockwises, it could have been jolly confusing.

It took until the late 1800s for Hove to be developed as Brighton, where the action was; the royalty at first, the grand early estates. Brighton even had a harbour and river if you go back far enough before both were infilled and hidden, much like the town's fishing heritage is today. Hove had little going for it – no harbour, river or distinguishing features. One pond, the Wick existed and was skated on when the winters were icy.

Part of the Western/Stanford land was due a huge development, called the 'West Brighton Estate', (despite being in what is technically Hove today) but it never happened. Despite the 1881 Stanford Estate Act being passed in Parliament, the only bit that was ever built was the grand yellow-brick hotel at the bottom east side of Grand Avenue in Hove. Hove was developed instead by a range of different developers, stretching initially all the way back to the railway line that had been laid forty years before.

One of the streets laid out next to the railway line, magnificently positioned looking down towards the sea, was Cromwell Road. This was where Clovis Chubb took over Holland House School that I was at back in 1925 and that I have just walked past. It's a grand street of three-story, bay-windowed Victorian villas, each ornately decorated and blessed with a decent-sized garden.

Holland House School was founded before the First World War in numbers 35 and 36 Cromwell Road by a Mr W. B. Cawood. It was a Boys' Prep School, established with the aims of training boys up for the Navy or preparing them for entry to senior public schools. Unfortunately for him and the school, Cawood was a member of the Territorials and so was called up to serve King and Country in India in the Great War, which is where he was killed.

One of the school's early pupils was the author Patrick Hamilton, who wrote the 'West Pier' trilogy of books, the first of which features boys at a Hove boarding school, of which Hove had many at that time. Hamilton attended with his brother, Bruce, from 1912 to 1914 but was moved to Colet Court School in Chiswick, which he despised and returned to Holland House as a boarder.

Hamilton was far more positive about the school than I was, but died young as a result of alcoholism. My doctors tell me I shall live to a ripe old age, thankfully as I avoid the bottle and have been a vegetarian since my early days. That was thanks in part to a certain woman whom I shall mention in due course,

Thanks to Hamilton though, the school was immortalised as 'Rodney House' in Hamilton's *The*

West Pier. Holland House's next head was C. R. de Lyons-Pike, whose name everybody managed to incorrectly pronounce. He was high church, bespectacled and unusually young for a Headmaster. He certainly wasn't eleven years old though, like me, nor was he determined to keep the school in Hove. In 1922, the year Hamilton published *The West Pier*, its Headmaster decided for some reason to move the school to Burgess Hill, nine miles away north of the Downs, north-east of Hove.

It became St Peter's Court school, and Holland House continued under its original name under the leadership of two joint Headmasters, 'CTJ' (Clovis) Chubb and 'HED' Townsend. Headmasters in those days all had to have three initials by law.

After my time, the school survived, in a fashion, under Chubb and moved to a house called Wick Lodge in Lansdowne Road. It continued there until it closed and my school moved there in its place instead. In its final years, it was forced to become eventually that sanctuary of the enemy to me in my early days – a *girls'* school. After he moved from Holland House, De Lyons-Pike 'retired' from teaching in 1927, despite being constantly referred to as 'young'. Perhaps the constant mispronunciation of his name aged him prematurely. Or perhaps it was girls. They do that.

Before my time, Hove seems to have had most school leaders in their thirties and forties, hardly young for the time. The youngest was a Rebecca Wharton who was aged twenty, who seems to have taken over their family-run school from her thirty-year old brother. A twenty-two-year old, one Mr Andrews, ran one of three schools in Upper Brunswick Place in the 1881 census. He 'received pupils to prepare [them] for public school' and lived with his mother, father, two sisters, two servants and six pupils.

Hove was a breeding ground for numerous small private schools, such as Mr Andrews' establishment once the land was developed. Long before I and the others opened the doors to Claremont School, there was a wealth of schools, the oldest run by a seventy-one-year old; someone a whole sixty years older than I. Hove was seen as a great place to educate young minds in a warm and sunny climate by English benchmarks. It was (and still is as far as I'm aware) only 51.5 miles from London Bridge Station and 52 from Victoria; with five trains an hour arriving at Hove's then six stations.

There was Hove, Aldrington, Portslade, West Hove, Rowan Halt and, the closest to Clovis Chubb's world of education, Holland Road Halt. Parents of wealthy students were told how Hove's schools could be reached from as far away by train as Liverpool, Birmingham and Manchester and the West Country. This was probably why by 1871, 10 per cent of the town's population were employed in the private education profession – that's 1,104 people if you like your numbers.

Hove was also attractive due to its pleasant temperatures. Its generous dose of 1,635.82 hours of sunshine in 1927 alone lead to only 37 inches of rain with an average maximum temperature of 57 degrees Fahrenheit. By 1935, Hove's population of 58,000 could enjoy the use of 29 lawn tennis courts, one meadow turf bowling green, 24 hand tennis courts, 5 Cumberland Turf bowling greens, 4 croquet lawns, 10 cricket and 10 football pitches. It boasted a Lido cinema by Hove Station and Hove Lagoon was open back then but was used for model yacht sailing and boating.

So it was no wonder Hove had so many private schools, from its very first in 1796 in Dr Morrell's Academy at the Wick to its peak in 1871 when there were 31. The number of schools grew as Hove developed and spread alongside and away from the sea. No wonder Isambard Kingdom Brunel, Eric Gill and RAB Butler would all be schooled here.

Most famously, Winston Churchill enjoyed his time here, with the proximity of his family doctor, as well as his ability to enjoy swimming and horseriding, helping the sickly boy who arrived here survive into adulthood. One day, the nation may thank Churchill for winning this war, and perhaps the nation will thank Hove for bringing Churchill back to health.

The proletariat were looked after too by Hove's teaching folk. A National School for poor people opened in George Street in 1858. But, to us moneyed folk (not that Father made enough for us to be truly moneyed with the amount Mother could spend), schools like that were half a world away, even if they were a street away from us. We went to our schools, they went to theirs. We went to our Holland Houses, schools where lack of ability in the staff was compensated by the network you had as an adult and the contacts that gave. Holland House School was a school that was part of a rich heritage of over a century of private education in the town, with a history dating back to the 1790s. It had employed MOB, it had educated Patrick Hamilton and now it had taken me in.

But it would lose both MOB and I back in 1925.

Lesson 3
Performance Rehearsals

Hemel Hempstead, 1939 and Hove, 1940

I am in Hove for a meeting later on that afternoon that I'll tell you about in a bit, but I need to pound the streets first for two reasons. First, it is to take my mind and memories back to 1925 and the events that led to me leaving Holland House but also to remind me of those early days at the Claremont so I can, I hope, talk about them with ease.

Actually, there's a third. MOB said when I visited him last year that I should come back and look at the old place and I think he might be right. I'm not quite ready for that though yet, so a cup of tea and a teacake sounds a good idea first.

I'm not nervous about seeing the place; nothing really bad ever happened to me at the Claremont. Quite the opposite in fact, it had been quite a low ebb in my life at that point just before my 12th birthday when we started up the school at Claremont House. It's just, I can't quite believe we did it; we pulled it off. I had no nerves it seemed back then. To an eleven-year-old (MOB was right about my age for once!), it was just something that *needed to be done.*

We are told we grow in confidence with age, and yet, I wish I had the nerves now in 1940 that I had back in 1925. It was such a big challenge and we pulled it off. I've never heard of anyone before, during or since who has managed to open their own school at an age before manhood started to knock on the door.

I mentioned my visit to MOB last year. Even last year, in the height of evacuation the trains were still good', thankfully, and, despite the disruptions of the war, even a lengthy journey to Hemel Hempstead wasn't too arduous. Quite why MOB ended up there for retirement is still quite beyond me, or his family, but then he always was an awkward bugger and probably just liked the sound of the place's name or (more likely) stuck a pin in a map. I think that was why he sent his son so far west to boarding school. He always found bizarrely-named English settlements amusing whenever he taught us geography.

MOB seemed to have visibly shrunk when I entered his room in the retirement lodge, not far from Hemel Hempstead station. He had always stooped slightly, but now he seemed to be folding into himself, like a pocket knife. Photos of his son, Bill, the current headmaster of Claremont and his family were positioned round the room but Mick always turned them round when he was drinking too much, which was always. Bill is even bigger than Mick was at his peak before the booze and illnesses pervaded.

"Did yer bring the bottle like I asked?" A whole year since I'd last seen him and that was his greeting. Johnnie Walker Red Label whisky was the entry fee to the wonderland of Mick O'Byrne. No bumper cars, or merry-go-rounds or bathing beauty competitions in this park, but you still needed your entry fee.

"Yes, Mick. Red Label, alright?" I opened the bedside cabinet and added it to the other large bottles of whisky and rum he would have conned staff each into bringing. Mick's family had fallen out with him back in 1928 and he had not seen them since. One bottle was already opened and had been tackled head on, despite it not yet being past eleven. The staff had evidently given up on trying to change his ways, same as we all had.

"A red label in the war was what they stuck on you if you were a dangerous hospital case; about to haemorrhage. Seems fitting for me these days, I suppose." He poured himself a large measure and looked at it, twisting the glass, as if to check for quality. "Are ye going back there?"

I nodded and explained my purpose there to him.

"It's not the same since we moved. I couldn'a taught in Wick Lodge. Big, draughty old place. At least Claremont House had a bit o' style. A grand house, so it was." MOB was referring to the school's new residence near Lansdowne Road, further east in Hove, which you may remember I mentioned earlier and was also known as St Michael's Hall. Mick's son, Bill, the current headmaster believed the south coast would soon be a danger zone, and I'd heard he had been looking at relocating to Berkshire, especially if *Sitzkrieg*, as the British press were calling it, changed into a real war and the Germans looked like they would soon be coming this way.

"At least you're only going to do a speech, Clifton."

He still called me that, despite me being twenty-six now. I was still a titchy adolescent to him, or at least that's what I thought. Mick saw people on a variety of levels, and sometimes in double vision too if it had been a heavy morning's drinking. *How on earth are you still alive?* I thought to myself as the November morning tried to break in through Mick's still-pulled curtains, or 'coitayns' as he had always pronounced them.

And why did I choose you of all people? Why did I let you lead the way my life would go? But then I always knew the answer to that question. He was the father I had wanted when Clifton Senior was ordered out of my life by my mother. My preferred choice of parent was no longer in my life back in 1925. So, I found a replacement and put him in charge of a school. This flawed, scarred and tortured man. He was also an engineer by trade; it was MOB that made me choose to follow his career pathway before Flanders Fields came calling.

"It's not like yer facing the best metal the Krupps factory made being fired at you at Passchendaele like I did, is it? You were just a rich little git who set up a school."

"I don't think my family were that rich, Mick." It was pointless to say things such as "I don't think you're being particularly fair, Mick", or "Do you realise that words can hurt, Mick?". He didn't work on that level – words were just clouds that passed, that could do you no harm, a sort of Irish opposite of the miasma theory. He rained on you – and you soaked it up and listened. That was all. Neither was he typical of Anglo-Irish men of his time, born in the late Victorian era. Conan Doyle, Wilde, and the others all seemed to shroud their Irish background; MOB wallowed in it and spoke more like a Dublin potboy than a schoolmaster, let alone a headmaster. They all emulated the Duke of Wellington, an earlier denier of Irish roots, whereas he effed and blinded like a navvie. The nearest Mick ever got to the Duke of Wellington was to drink in the pub of that name by Brighton Station.

MOB seemed to sense my thoughts and his frosty front softened a tad. "Just tell it like it was, Clifton. Tell of Holland House, and Chubb. Tell of Ross and how you and Payne got the money together, found the place, how you got it off the ground. That summer at the Paynes. How Eileen fed yer and cleaned yer rich backsides."

He looked sad at the mention of his wife, who was miles away and still involved with the school. There was moisture amongst the sticky white gloop in the folds at the sides of his eyes. "Tell them of the dog, and the swimming and the football and the lessons but most of all Clifton, most of all, tell them about the cricket. You mustn't miss out the cricket."

He looked around the room. "We didn't achieve that much in terms of the world," and here he could be looking around his drab room and referring to his meagre possessions, "but we won at cricket in the grounds of what was once the cricket club of a king. And that, Clifton, is something." He picked up the reversed picture of Bill when he was a professional cricketer, before he became Claremont's headmaster, turned it round and rubbed the smeared glass front with a tobacco-stained thumb.

Mick was referring to the place we spent more time at than in the classroom, the Sussex County Cricket Ground, which could trace its roots back to George IV's cricket ground in Ireland's Pleasure Ground, partly on what is now the Level park in Brighton.

George had been Prince George when he had played there in the late eighteenth century, and MOB always made a detour there when in Brighton and to drink at the nearby *Bat and Ball* pub on Ditchling Road. For an Irish Catholic who refused to give up his roots, accent or mannerisms, Mick O'Byrne was a staunch monarchist and savoured any reference to the Royal Family.

Douglas Payne, my best friend at Holland and Claremont had once asked Mick: "But aren't they German?" during a history lesson and had experienced a hefty history textbook narrowly miss his right ear. It was remarkable any of our schoolbooks at Holland House had any covers left.

"Where do I start?" I queried? My military career was in its infancy; I had little experience at that stage of speaking in public.

"You start..." MOB smiled. "You start, with what brought you to that hole that was Holland House."

I winced inside. That was one area of my life I hadn't thought about for a long time.

Lesson 4
House Assembly

Hove, 1940 and 1925

That meeting with MOB last already seems a lifetime ago. When I arrived back in Sussex this year, Bill O'Byrne had kindly offered me bed and board with his family in Preston Park Avenue but I had pleasantly refused as I thought I would need the time pacing the old streets to reconnect with the town and categorise my collection of thoughts into some sort of offer.

The meeting at Claremont (well, I call it a meeting, but Bill wants me to talk to the pupils) is on my mind so I have diverted to a café in Palmeira Square, as I mentioned, for some strong tea.

I rehearsed my thoughts.

Good morning, boys. My name is Bernard McCarthy Clifton and I started up this school, which was still called the Claremont School back in 1925, although it used to be in Second Avenue. This happened as I needed a school for my last year before my scholarship and thought I could put one together that was better than my previous school.

That previous school, Holland House Prep, wasn't the best run school in Hove. I would have had to leave anyway as I was eleven and my prep school days were ending, but I walked out just before my twelfth birthday, which was May 30 1925. I was born in 1913 in 22 Brunswick Place and had to join Holland House as we could no longer afford my previous school.

The reason for this was my parents separated in 1925 and the money left just about covered my fees.

I left Holland House because...

I stopped at that point. A gramophone record was playing somewhere behind the square and the sound was carrying through the open rear window of the café. It was Rossini.

My mother always played Rossini, because she said it took her back to the time when she sang minor parts of what she called his greatest work; the ethereal *La Scala*. Its frenetic and passionate march was now resoundingly pounding in my ear canal, and my mother was standing at her dressing table, her chiffon dressing gown flowing down to the floor; her frail arm hinged with a cigarette clamped firmly in cigarette holder. The smoke flowed and swirled like a gentle tornado. I was watching from the landing once more as Father remonstrated with her.

"You are not a provider, Bernard. You're a shadow of a man, do you hear? A shadow." Bernard was my father's middle name, like mine and like me he used it rather than his first name of Brendan. It was a habit of some Anglo-Irish families like ours.

"I wouldn't need to provide so much, Estelle, if you spent less. I could bring home the wealth of Rockefeller and you would dribble it away. You spend and spend and spend."

"When a man is so devoid of charm and lacking in emotional integrity as you are, then a woman is entitled to trifles, dalliances and distractions to maintain herself."

"I am well aware what your distractions include at the moment, Estelle. You have made your entertainment, oh so public. You have lost all respect from our community, our friends all have disdain for you!"

"Our friends don't see the weakling of a man I married."

"A weakling would not take the action I am now, Estelle. I am past the point of all rational care. You can see how you provide for yourself and the boy on the wage of a failed musician, which is what you are."

My mother realised she had pushed Father too far, but this was not the first of these rants. It was always the same; he didn't bring in enough money; she spent too much of it. Providing and provision was always the theme and it applied not just to money, but in other ways that an eleven-year old boy was only barely aware of. As he walked out, the word 'provision' seemed to hang in the air. I was no longer to be provided with a father; my future would now be an empty and more lonely one. My preferred parent would no longer be in my life.

I realised I had finished my tea and had been scraping the base of the cup across the cusp of the saucer, its gold gilt already frayed and chipped. The afternoon I had spent at Douglas's house at 57 Langdale Gardens, following the book throwing incident,, came to mind. His mother had always had teacups with a golden gilt edge too.

"Bernard! How lovely to see you!" Josephine Payne was always effusive in her greeting; warm, welcoming and wonderful. There were none of the silences in their house that pervaded the air in ours. I was best friends with Douglas Payne for many reasons. He was a slightly plump, blond, jovial fellow who giggled infectiously at the slightest cause.

He had a large collection of First World War model aircraft that he was willing to share with you and we had recreated many an air battle when younger. His family made you feel happy and cared for. His Father, Austin Payne, was a famous cartoonist for the *Daily Mirror* and we would spend hours with his Pa inking and sketching in his studio when he was in town. But most of all, Douggie's homelife was the homelife I yearned for and had never really had.

Douggie's father was rarely there as his hours at the *Mirror* were long, and the family had another seaside home at Herne Bay. However, when he came through the door a happy home became happier and your life became fuller. He would produce cough candy and winter clove sweets from behind your ears at a rate of knots. He would always bring home from London the latest toy and would always insist on a game of rugger in the hallway before any meal could commence.

If a picture or family portrait got broken in the process, Austin Payne would always then shout (much to his wife's displeasure): "Never liked the blighter –

anyway!" It became a catchphrase and one we used much as other people quoted catchphrases from comedy shows on the Light Programme.

"What have you terrible boys been doing with yourselves then?" Josephine, or Josie as she allowed me to call her, was pouring tea into the golf-rimmed cups as we helped ourselves to manor house fruit cake, the afternoon after I had come into contact with that lengthily-named algebra book.

"Bern's been practicing his heading skills." Douggie giggled as he chomped on a particularly large wedge of cake, a glazed cherry hanging out of the left side of his mouth. It dropped onto his knee and he tried to kick it back in his mouth with the rest of the partly-chewed cake.

"Really, Bernard, I thought Mr Chubb wasn't particularly fond of soccer?" Josie Payne was already refilling my cup after two sips. 'Boys need refreshment' was one of her catchphrases, and also a mantra she adhered to whenever we turned up at Doug's place in Grand Avenue. The red brick and terracotta mansion was only thirty years old and still looked brand new. It was a small, cosy new house full of warm carpets, rugs and throws.

The furniture was dotted about so that the inhabitants of the house were always encouraged to talk, joke, play and laugh together. You didn't go to the Paynes' for solitary time. You went to refresh your soul and recharge your joie de vivre.

"It wasn't a football, Mama, Bernie failed to dodge a lob from MOB. He was in hurling mood again."

Josie Payne laughed. "He is a terror! Was his aim better than usual, Bernie?"

I lifted up my fringe of dark, sharply cut hair to show my small bruise on my temple and laughed. "Irish shotput champion of 1907 I reckon."

"That's pretty good for old Mick. He obviously has been cutting back on the kerosene. Imagine how many Fritz in the trenches survived as they had Mick chucking Mills bombs at them! We'd have finished the war in 1915 if he'd have been a better shot."

She was now passing a jar of crystallised ginger over to me, which was a particular favourite of mine. It seemed to sum up their household. It was sweet, warm, orange, sparkling and tickled your stomach inside. I savoured the crystallised squares of sugar that coated the ginger cube on my tongue, rubbing my tongue backwards and forwards across the rough surface before biting down hard on the warming ginger chunk. I imagined myself safe and warm, a minute crystal of sugar, snug in the cube of ginger.

"Bern's been talking rot, though, since then, Mama. Says he's going to become a Chubber himself." Chubber was our codeword for our Headmaster, Clovis Chubb.

"Is that right, Mr Clifton, Sah? Fancy a gown and mortarboard do you, taking assemblies and morningsong? Shouting at boys and telling old Mick what to do?" Josie would always tease and prod you with a wide smile and a gentle hint of mockery, whilst never smothering any boyhood dreams you mentioned. To her, anything was possible and you could make it there. To my mother, money was needed for her dreams of higher society, travel and her desires to be taken seriously as a musician again. Anyone who didn't have money to help her in her plans was surplus to requirements. That included me, I had always been sure.

"Not a Chubber as such, Josie. I was just wondering what it would be like to run your own school, more as a... senior partner really. MOB's lob got me thinking why more children don't set up their own schools, where we choose our staff, lessons, activities and so on. They're meant to be there for children, so I wondered why adults don't consult us."

"That blow to your head has had an impact, hasn't it? Your problem as always, Bernie, is that you're applying intellect to the whole process. You can't have THINKING involved in the creation of schools. They are merely capsules of sterility whereby adults ensure that their hideous offspring, such as my Douglas are subjected to the same entrenched horrors we faced when we were small, frightful creatures too. Each generation has a responsibility to pass on the pain, torture, boredom and dullness that it undertook. You really are being a bit selfish here Bernard, old stick. Fancy wanting to miss out on all of that!"

A wry smile was forming on the side of her face. The same side, I noticed that Douglas had yet more crumbs of cake stuck to.

"On a serious note though, you only have a few months left of prep and then you two elderly warriors hit the seniors. Just keep your head down, mind

MOB's bowling arm and you'll be fine."

"MOB's fine. I'm happy to take any amount of blows to the head if it means I'm in his classes and not the other masters'. Peterson, for example fell asleep whilst reading out his own notes last week."

"Bern's right, Ma. Vaughan and Verdoake make me sleepy just by looking at them. If it wasn't for Pearl and MOB, I'd have gone do-lally long before now." Douggie made a face of a demented rabbit with crossed eyes and his large front teeth hanging over his bottom lip.

We burst into song:

Holland House, Holland House,
we're led by a timid mouse,
Called Clovis Chubb who's short and gummy,
and his rather scary Mummy.
She won him in a game of gin rummy.

Peterson, he falls asleep,
Verdoake, his lessons are quite weak,
and Vaughan can't teach for toffee.
If you're gonna come here........
We recommend coffee!

Josie Payne giggled in the infectious way she always did and then lit up a slender cigarette at the end of her cigarette holder. "You reckon you could do better than Chubb then, Bernard?" she asked in all seriousness.

"I bet he could, Ma," said Douglas. "You know how

sharp he is, his inventions, his events he organises at the Corn Exchange. Bern's a future *Leader of Men!*" Each word punctuated with gravitas. He stood up and saluted me.

"In that case then, James Bernard McCarthy Clifton," Josie grinned, also saluting. "We hereby challenge you, before the summer to have in place a new school that befits a *Leader of Men* like yourself and even the stripling puppet of a son I have in front of me. I command you to find a place for my runt of the litter here!"

"You're on!" I saluted, ready to play Josie Payne at her own game, marvelling at the fact she hadn't just claimed how absurd I'd been to entertain the notion, as my own mother would have. I would show her a small boy, with the help of one daft friend could get together a better team of teachers than Chubb had managed, and without the help of my mother closely observing my every move, just as he had. A few letters here and there, a few telephone calls pretending to be a recruiting headmaster, the odd advert....

Let's see where this takes us, I said to myself.

"Pull this off, Headmaster Clifton," mused Josie, looking up at the ceiling before spinning around and grabbing me by jacket collars, and we will stump up half your costs. Austin's looking for a new project to fund Douglas's inheritance on. You might just be it."

I gulped inwardly. This intellectual exercise had suddenly become a reality. I felt I couldn't now let Josie Payne down; things had gone too far.

"Remember, Mr Clifton, it is not that final date on

your gravestone that matters. It is what is represented by the hyphen between that and your year of birth. It's not who we are in this life that matters, or even what we choose to do; it is sometimes what happens at the time we do it."

I nodded and raised my teacup. "What shall we drink to?"

Josie and Douglas stood up too, cups in hand.

"To a school where intellectual snobbery will reign but social snobbery is banned." Josie was looking towards the clouds out the window as she spoke. "Where as many pupils as possible earn scholarships for further education and become the great minds of the future! Where we don't just say, but *do* – in order to have a great soul!"

"Magnum fac animum habeas!" Douggie shouted, always a whizz with his Latin, despite his poor teaching.

"Amen!" I said and Douggie and I clinked our cups. As Sherlock Holmes had said, the game was afoot!

The next morning, I awoke not entirely sure how serious Douggie's Mother had been, and more importantly, how serious I was. I did know that, however, school was most definitely not for me and that persuading Mother of my ownership of some malady before she left for her social appointments for the day was necessary.

Douglas was also, conveniently, struck down with a debilitating disease that day and that was why we were both by nine thirty that morning on the train up to Devil's Dyke, a steep dry chalk valley next to a peak on the South Downs chain of hills, north of Brighton and Hove. If you've never walked along these hills, they are like a huge green backbone that separates coastal from inland Sussex. Kipling compared them to whales, but they remind me more of a green counterpane being shaken out and drifting in the air before settling. They are smooth, gentle, green and reassuring.

We left the station and walked the few hundred yards to the summit. The ruins of an old brick outhouse faced the Weald to the north, the Dyke Hotel to the east, the Downs to the west and the towns of Brighton and Hove below. We sat on the top of the brick wall.

"What we doing then, Bern?"

"Perspective, Douggie, old man, perspective. From here, we get a sense of it. We live in Hove and so need to see how far in all directions the school could be from home. From here we can see Sussex and Surrey; whether we site the school on a hill high up or down low. Whether we want it in a green area with lush fields, to stimulate and improve young minds, in wooded areas for science, near footpaths for hiking or by the sea for coastal fieldwork."

"Could we not just have it in Hove?"

"Oh, s'pose so."

"This was a bit of a waste of time really Bern, wasn't it?"

"Yes. I think you're right."

Two hours later, having decided we would stick

with what we know, we were outside the office of a lettings and estate agent at the top of Adelaide Crescent. *Willett, Lindless and Overton* proudly displayed their architectural wares in their window for all to see.

"Gentlemen. Whatever is the reason behind you frequenting my shop with your presence?" Mr Willett wasn't used to having children come unaccompanied into his realm. "Are you undertaking research of some kind for your school?"

He peered down at us through both his half-moon spectacles and a haze of arrogance. He had limpid, inquisitive eyes set in a hawkish face, with a sloping forehead, a long nose and the merest hint of a turn to his lips. He had missed a small patch to the left of his mouth when shaving that morning.

"No, we want to start one." I came straight out with my aim. The less we beat about the bush, and the sooner we could convince Willett and get ourselves on the next rung of the ladder, a property to start our school in. Staff and pupils would be easier to recruit if we had somewhere to show them.

"Gentlemen, as much as I like a 'wizard prank' like this as you young folk call them, I am a busy man and have a number of clients, moneyed, respectable and mature clients to see today. Now if you..."

"We have money." Douggie interjected.

"Pocket money, boys, will not be enough to rent or buy a property in our fair town. Now, if you would be..."

"We have money." Douggie again calmly insisted.

"Children, mere children, do not bankroll schools." Willets straightened both his glasses and mousey-brown moustache simultaneously. It gave the illusion that his head wobbled.

"What if they did?" It was my turn to speak now. "What if two boys were the vanguard, the pathfinders for a new business? It was only in our grandfathers' time, in Victoria's age that children younger than us worked on the streets, in factories, in offices, on warships. Why should youths not also be leaders of business, the managers, the entrepreneurs? Is this not the age where we believe in evolution; in the improvement of species? Why can children not jump the chasm from sheep to shepherd? Why must we judge a man's success within the boundaries of manhood? Have boy kings not led their men into battle? Did not ten-year-old midshipmen lead grown men into battle?"

"Hear the boy." I had been unaware that Josephine Payne had come into the shop whilst I was in mid flow. "If anyone could start up a school, it is this boy here. Clifton is an inventor. He creates things. Even at the age of six he was building contraptions in our garden. What is a school if not an invention? You build gadgets, machinery by assembling them and seeing they work together. How is that different from a school? One gets together adults, children, equipment and you get them to work together. We are putting together the machinery and the workers; we just need a factory building to house them."

"Madam, I..."

"Can you find us a property, or can't you? My husband works for the *Daily Mirror* and has an account at Coutts Bank and has said he will cable any funds you need for the initial outlay."

"May I ask what position he holds? We don't lease property to any old print worker you know, who thinks they have a bit of clout just because one of those unions are on the move."

He spat the word 'union' out almost as if it was a particularly unpleasant sweet leaving an unwelcome taste in his mouth.

Josie pulled herself up straight. "My husband is Austin Bowen Payne, who illustrates the *Children's Mirror*. Six years ago he wrote *Pip, Squeak and...*"

"...Wilfred. It is my children's favourite, Mrs Payne. Is it true he named Wilfred after his Batman in the war?"

"Yes," Josie smiled. "Wilfred was a dear Batman, We still have him visit. He is particularly fond of Austin's artwork he created for him."

Willet's posture and attitude changed completely and the room seemed to warm. A glimmer of a smile appeared in the right side of his mouth.

"How many children would the school contain?"

It struck me at that point that the answer to Willets' question was not one I had entertained any thought to.

"Fourteen. At first. Thirty by its third year."

It was time for a random answer. Not a round number, but one that sounded as if dedicated thought had been put aside to it.

"Seven juniors and seven seniors initially. We will grow the school to 28 pupils or more by its third year. We will need a decent-sized building with gardens and probably three floors." This was becoming easier, the more I started talking!

"The staff will need in-house accommodation and there must be dining facilities for both boys and masters." Where was this coming from? Wherever it was coming from in the recesses of my mind, it was doing the trick. Willets' eyes had moved up and to the left, a sign MOB had once told us of a mind accessing either its memory or creating falsehoods.

Willets launched across the room with surprising grace and opened a cabinet drawer.

"I might just have the place for you." He said.

Willets met us later that day at the corner of Church Road and Second Avenue. Its very name gave a clue to its air of opulence and splendour; its location had the honour of being the salubrious sandwich filling between Hove's Grand Avenue and First Avenue. Second Avenue was nearer the sea than Holland House and the wide road was graced with matching, elegant, lofty, yellow-brick Italianate Victorian villas along either side. At the southern end was the Kingsway (our stretch of the coastal road), the promenade and the sea. MOB later told us the history of the street and every word remains with me; he had that ability.

I never realised until later on that the houses were the same colour and style as Holland House; they must have had the same architects and builders. It made the new school reassuring for the pupils we later pinched from Chubb, I guess.

The first record we think we have of the street is a deed from 1856 that mentions a new road from Turnpike Road, as the Kingsway was then known up to Wilbury Road, as it is today, or Long Barn Farmhouse as it was before the development of the Stanford Estate. Looking at a map today, we presume that this must have followed the line of what is now Second Avenue. As I mentioned earlier, Dame Ellen Stanford sold off the land in 1869 when she came of age so the Stanford Estate could be built. Although it didn't conform to the original plans for a uniform-looking estate, some of Hove's grandest Victorian architecture would be erected on Grand, First, Second, Third and Fourth Avenues including the palatial Kings and Queens Mansions.

The West Hove Development company was formed and developed the Avenues in Hove (First, Second, Grand, Third and Fourth) and instructed a well-known builder,, William Willett,, to build the properties. We were about to discover it would be his descendant, whom we had just met, and would show us around. Like Thomas Cubitt in Brighton, once the building was done, estate agency would instead provide an income for these building firms.

Willett was not from Brighton and Hove, but built many grand houses across London and the South East. For a house to be 'Willett-built' was a mark of quality and luxury. He was a fascinating character, and one of the earliest advocates of British daylight saving time. He died, unfortunately too early to see it being brought in during World War I, a year later in 1916.[1]

By 1887, ten houses had already been built in the street, with more on the way and the first house ever re-sold, in 1896 went for the princely sum of £6,500. By 1881 the street was formally opened as a public highway and perhaps in response to this, its residents were petitioning the council that elm trees were planted. In the First World War, one of the residents, Mr Lewis Woolf, temporarily donated his house in the street in aid of the war and it became the Headquarters for the Prisoners Of War Invalid Comfort Fund. Soon after Claremont School moved out of Second Avenue, the road's first hotel opened up at No. 15, by a Mrs K. M. Phelp. Back in 1925, we were focussing on a home for our burgeoning idea, this school that was rapidly becoming a reality rather than a whim, rather than hospitality.

Willett walked the three of us down the leafy boulevard, its elm trees now maturing 45-odd years on and adding further to the air of respectability the street eschewed. Did we have the right to inflict a dozen or more children into the neighbourhood of these good folk? My doubts were soon overcome with

[1] *He is also the great-great grandfather of Chris Martin from Coldplay. Perhaps the inspiration for the song 'Clocks'?*

the argument that schools existed all over Hove; what was one more?

Number 13 Second Avenue was only two dwellings down from the north end of the street. It had three stories above ground and what looked like a large basement below. It was a double-fronted, symmetrical Italianate villa, with balanced bay windows on all three upper floors. The rooms looked large; the ceilings high and most of all, it looked welcoming. If a house had a human face, then this one had a friendly, open one. It reminded me of a bricks-and-mortar version of Douggie's face.

"Claremont House has been vacant for five weeks now." Willett was looking down his file of details on the building as the word 'Claremont' looked up at me from the decorative pillars at the start of the tessellated tiled pathway to the door.

"Seven bedrooms across the two upper floors. A large rear garden, kitchen, servants' quarters and superbly decorated as my father's craftsmen managed so well. None of the dreary attempts of building we have witnessed since the war."

"I like the name." I said. I couldn't explain why, it just had an Irish ring to it that suited me just fine. MOB was originally from County Clare; perhaps this was a good sign. There was also some other message my PMM was trying to deliver from my subconscious to the conscious part. Something about staffing; someone I was starting to realise the school couldn't work without.

The building had a warmth to it as well. It may have looked similar to the terraced yellow-brick houses Holland House had been based in, but I couldn't get over how it seemed to have a bit of a human face to it. Perhaps it might have been the fact it was double-fronted; bay windows either side of the door over three floors but I was sure it was smiling down at me.

I think this was more than due to the look; houses are happy places when they've had happy owners. It is said one theory about the causes of supernatural activity is that houses 'record' human activity of great emotion, violence or anger, so it must make sense that happy ownership leads to a happy atmosphere or feel to a building.

"It's only ever been in the hands of one family," Willett said proudly. "Before we finished its construction, Claremont was originally purchased by Joseph Peters. Joseph Peters was a very well-respected carriage-maker, who always wanted to live by the sea. His wife, however felt slightly differently and only wished to live in London so it must have been a large place for Peters.

It wasn't to stay that way, though. It was part of the marriage settlement for one of Joseph Peters' daughters – Emily Gertrude Peters when she married Walter Knapp-Appleyard in 1886. He was a Yorkshire tanner who had successfully patented a design for a fleshing machine for treating leather. The couple initially made their home in Headingly, Leeds in a house named Claremont where their three children – Violet Cecily, Claude Peters and Vernon Peters were all born. However, during the final years of the nineteenth Century, the leather business declined and economic conditions turned against them. The result was that, in 1902, Walter Knapp-Appleyard's tannery business went into liquidation. Walter Knapp-Appleyard having to do jury service in Leeds in that year can't have helped much, either.

Family anecdotes have it that on learning of this situation, Joseph Peters – who was a devoted family man – wrote to Knapp-Appleyard offering him 'a small house in Hove' in which to live and from which to manage the properties that by that time Joseph Peters had acquired in that vicinity. They lived in a house in Cromwell Road, but would eventually inherit this house from Peters and decided to import the name of their Yorkshire home to this one where their children had been born."

Willett then went on to explain how, a generation later, the children were now grown and each living in different parts of Peters' portfolio of housing. Since the war, servants were thinner on the ground and grand houses were harder to maintain. The Peters family was now too large for any one family within it to claim ownership of 13 Second Avenue and it was likely it would eventually be subdivided, like many others in the road had already.

The house in Leeds was not unique in having this name. I later found out that there had been a fashion in the nineteenth century of giving places the name Claremont after the great estate in Esher, Surrey that Queen Victoria had been fond of. The house there was originally built for the architect and Restoration dramatist Sir John Vanbrugh who sold it to his friend, the Earl of Clare, future Duke of Newcastle, who originally named it 'Clare-Mount'.

Clive of India bought the house and rebuilt it using his fortune from his time in India, with such names as Henry Holland, designer of George IV's original Brighton Pavilion working on the building and Lancelot 'Capability' Brown working on its gardens.

The building in Esher seemed cursed for a while. Clive committed suicide in 1774; although not at Claremont. George IV's one and only daughter, Princess Charlotte died there during childbirth. The surgeon in question, Sir Richard Croft refused to use the latest technology of the time and the baby was left agonisingly inside her for ten hours. He later committed suicide as a reaction to his bungling. Without Charlotte's death, though, Victoria would never have been given use of Claremont by Charlotte's husband, Leopold, who was Victoria's favourite uncle and who eventually became King of the Belgians. Nor would Victoria have become Queen and made the house and its gardens the height of fashion once again, and the name used all over the country in celebration. Former French King, Louis Phillipe and his wife, Queen Amelie, lived there in exile after the French Revolution of 1848.

Not that we knew it back in 1925, but Claremont in Esher had already had a 'Claremont School' in the building. In the Great War it was briefly used as a convalescent home, like many great houses. Then in 1916 it was first lent to a girls' school from Leatherhead and by 1922 it became Claremont School. It was no longer in the hands of the nobility as it had been passed down from Queen Victoria to the Duke of Saxe-Coburg, who had the poor judgement to serve as a German general in the Great War, so it was confiscated by the government.

By 1923, the first principal of the school, Mrs Packer, moved it to Norwood, where it remained until 1931 when she returned to Claremont, and it ran as Claremont again. We would be the only Claremont School in Sussex, however, and that was enough for me. We had a building, and now we had a name too.

Lesson 5
Economics

Hove, 1925

Doug and I were up at Devil's Dyke again, but this time we would have a more purposeful visit. We were walking from the Dyke to a nearby golf course, where we would find the man who had helped split my parents up, and he was going to pay for it. Financially, I mean. I wasn't a member of one of Brighton's razor gangs, or the Victorian Trunk Murderer. I wasn't sure how the meeting would go, so as we walked along the top of the backbone of Sussex, its Downland, I was glad Douglas was making conversation so my mind was occupied with the day before, and not the day ahead.

"What did you think of the house then Bern? I thought it was smashing. Pokes Holland House squarely in the eye."

"We just need to pay for it now, Douggie. Until we get the first fees in. Your father's money will cover the deposit and the furniture, not the rent or the wages."

"Is that where Ross will come in?"

"Ahum. If he coughs up."

"Do you think he will?"

"Depends. On how guilty he feels, how much money he's won of late and whether or not we can be

44

persuasive."

Alexander, or Alec Ross, was a professional golfer, playboy and, in my eye, a philanderer. He was also ludicrously wealthy and was known for his generosity. Whether that generosity would stretch to the son of one of his pursuits was another matter. I had only met him once and was under the impression I might flee the golf course with a putter imprinted into my cranium and with a few ribs less than intact. I changed the subject back to the house again.

Or rather, its garden. Being boys we focussed on possibilities for sports first "The garden's not big enough for games." I pondered. We'll need to find a big garden for rugger and footie.

"What about the Cricket Ground? Belmont School hire it out already I've heard."

"MOB will love that. Douggie, what do you think about MOB as the Headmaster?"

"Depends how much booze we can get our hands on to bribe him. Don't know, Bern, old man. He's a smashing teacher, idiosyncrasies and all, but can you see him running a school?"

"I think so – woah, look Douggie, a woodpecker!" One swooped along the hilltop road following our path, its green breast glistening as it reflected the late spring sun. It seemed that whole year was a sunny one. It may just be rose tinted spectacles, but I cannot recall a gloomy day.

During our visit to Claremont, before reaching the garden though, we had walked up the front steps and in through the main entrance with Willets. It was suitably grand enough to impress prospective families looking to spend their cash on their beloved offspring. The house may have been just a Victorian-built home, but it was a grand one, with lofty, ornately decorated ceilings, a delicately proportioned exterior and a feel of friendliness but genteelness. The room to the left of the main hall had a dumb waiter and felt like it could be a dining room. Behind it was a study and toilet, looking down on the gardens. To the right of the hallway was a large room, that we had decided would be the classroom/lecture theatre and meeting room; a small drawing room in front of that looked out over Second Avenue.

Looking back on it now, being grubby eleven-year olds, who weren't then interested in the fairer sex, and never thought of girls attending, we never thought much about bathing facilities. This would come back to haunt pupils later on when they came back from soccer or rugger covered in mud, but it wasn't a priority to us at that stage. Downstairs we had toilets, a downstairs kitchen where the domestics could prepare the meals, a recreation room and dining room for boarders and most importantly we felt, a room for hobbies and skills such as carpentry. It was important, Doug and I felt. to keep the thickies busy too.

Upstairs on the first floor would be a range of teachers' and boarders' bedrooms. We never thought of looking up on the second floor, as that was where domestics usually lived in our experience, but it ended up being for boarders as well. Bikes would be stored downstairs in the front garden and we decided that boys would enter that way, hang up outdoor coats and shoes in the basement, eat and then start the day's lessons on the first floor. The main entrance would be for staff, parents and founders only - us. Douggie would have the honour of pupil No.1. I had decided that I was to be, not a number, but instead a founding partner, who would give out the numbers to fellow boys. Josie Payne had also informed us that she would house any staff we could gather together over the summer as an incentive and so we could concentrate on getting together any resources and orders needed, which was great news.

"Here we are." I stated the obvious as we walked past the 'Dyke Golf Course' sign that marked the entrance to the golf club which had dominated the top of this part of the Downs, looking benevolently down on the Waterhall Valley below where I had played many games of hide-and-seek with Douggie when we were young squeakers.

"We're here to see Alec Ross," Douggie announced to the receptionist, hoping the familiar tone would convince that we knew him intimately.

"And he wants to see you why?" The ginger-haired young man with inflamed gums manning the reception desk looked at us both intently in turn.

"He's my stepfather." The lie came incredibly easily from my lips.

We were ushered out to the course by one of the caddies and taken to the seventeenth hole, where Ross was apparently coaching a local businessman. I hadn't realised until then just how much Ross resembled

MOB, nor that I didn't know his first name.

"James Clifton?" It appeared he knew mine, though. "What are you doing here?"

"I wondered if I could talk to you." My courage faltered, and my voice sounded small, reedy and hollow. For the first time I wondered if I was horribly out of my depth and whether this had all been a ghastly mistake. If we didn't get funding from Ross or some other funder, the Paynes, despite their wealth wouldn't be able or willing to bankroll a whole school for more than a month or two. We needed funding and then fees.

I thought he was about to shout at me but he remained calm. "Let me finish off here, and I'll meet you in the clubhouse in 15 minutes. Get these boys some ginger beer." He instructed the caddy in his gentle Scottish burr.

Five minutes later two very happy, small boys, one 11 and one 12 years of age were sat with large glasses of ginger beer with ice cream floats, guzzling away happily at these and ravaging a plate of ginger thins as we gazed out at the golfers on the first and eighteenth holes.

"Bit of a ginger theme here at this place, Bern," giggled Douggie, "Ginger pop, ginger thins and even a ginger receptionist!" I rocked back and forth with laughter. The fellow at reception in question glared at us.

"What theme should Claremont School have then?" I mused to Douggie. "I say, if we're not going down the ginger route, let's do flies. I rather like them.

Squashed fly biscuits, flying fish for supper and we all have our flies open?" Douggie guffawed loudly, causing two elderly gents, who evidently hadn't played golf since the Crimean War, judging by the look of them, to scowl at us.

"In all seriousness," my friend said, "as long as we don't have cauliflower every day like we do at Holland House, "I will be one happy chappie."

"I quite like cauliflower, as long as it's in cheese. It's beef I can't stand." I winced and squinted as I thought of the rancid beef we were served at school. The great globules of saggy fat that seemed to permeate every mouthful. The gristle and jelly it seemed to include. The undercooked bloody servings; the overcooked tough ends of the malodorous chunks we seemed to get which took your teeth minutes to break down. Worst of all were the tubes, though. I'm sure you know what I mean. Whether in a roast, or bully beef, it's those tough little white tubes that were once part of the poor beast's internal workings; its veins or valves or whatever they are.

I'm sure I should be more technical but I really don't want to investigate or look into it closer; nor do I want to dedicate any more fault. I just know that I've never once enjoyed a plate of any part of a cow, nor will I ever. I could quite happily do without it, or any other meatstuff, for the rest of my life.

"What about lessons?" I asked. "We have the chance to decide what young minds need. What do you reckon?"

"I can't see any families signing up the product of

their loins unless we offer the basics. The three Rs – reading, 'riting and 'rithmetic; and then the classics and the arts – history, geoggers, that sort of thing." I nodded in agreement.

"But no Latin," said Douglas stated. "I find it really easy, but I've had any desire to learn that sucked from my soul at Holland House. For a dead language, it doesn't 'alf go on and on." I saluted my friend. I was more than happy with that decision. "What else?" He asked.

"Well, when it comes to churchified matters you're as much of an unbeliever as I am," I added. "So let's play down the whole God thing too. The amount of time children waste on all that gutrot is a crime."

"Shan't hear me moaning on that front." Douggie mused. "I think MOB said something churchified once, but he's not one of the bible-addicted types, so I think we're safe on that front." We raised our glasses and toasted once more. This school founder role was becoming one that evidently needed toasting a lot.

"What are you two toasting?" Ross appeared behind us, surprising us both. He had evidently got rid of his client speedily.

"Beef every day, cauliflower, lots of religion and the endless study of Latin!" said Douggie.

Alec Ross third from left at the 1904 US Open (Wikipedia). *Below:* **Douglas Ross (DR Society).**

Donald Ross in 1905 (Wikipedia).

On the train back, we were both quite quiet, which was unusual for us. Douggie's mind had taken on the project as much as I had and was trying to process all we'd achieved in such a short time. He was planning the next steps, I could tell.

Me? The meeting with Ross had hit me hard to be honest. This was the man who had helped cause my father to depart and it made me realise deeply how much I missed Pa. I had lost all contact since the day he left and it ached in me throughout. Had I been a few years older and adolescence kicking in more at that stage, I would be blaming my mother heavily and the injustice of the world in general. Truth was though, I had been pretty much anaesthetised by Father leaving at that stage and that age. I'm not always the sharpest tool in the box in some ways and emotions usually hit me years after the event.

I think, to be honest, I was possibly going up to the golf course with the intention of letting Ross sense my displeasure in some way. I think I wanted him to know I knew all about him and Mother; that he had caused my father to leave and me to feel this listless and numb way I did now. Had he not wanted to hand over his loot, I think I subliminally had him pegged as my new arch-villain, the man who dared to stop my impossible dream.

He hadn't, though. Alec Ross was bored of being a professional golfer and wanted a temporary new project whilst back in Britain. He also wanted an investment – he had frittered much of his golf winnings away and a school, if it was run well, could after all be a profitable affair. It could pay for him to save up enough to make it back to America once more.

We also had our first member of staff. I never would have predicted it, but Ross was to be our first master.

Lesson 6
Parents' Evening

Hove, 1925

The evening of May 29 witnessed my mother, Estelle Elena Clifton being busy preparing her looks for a musical soiree she was due to attend. My birthday (the following day) was lower down her list of priorities than her evening excursion tonight, as she would usually sleep the whole day after a night on the town.

Tonight before her departure would be the only chance I would get to talk to her for some days. This was because, following a day asleep, she became fixated on her woes; hitting a low ebb where she focussed on her career, her financial worries and what might have been. I found her terribly boring, I must be honest. Conversations we had on the rare occasions we were in the house together were one-sided and involved her talking about pieces of music she loved, or composers she had met or sung for at great and detailed length. I could have been setting up an opium den or a prison camp, or even an opium den in a prison camp, and she would not have been particularly bothered.

"Oh James, there you are." I detested the way she said my name, with a dip before the 'a' so it came out as 'Jiames'. "Manhandle my chiffon scarf will you this way? No, the turquoise one next to the mirror."

"I want to talk to you, Mama." She had been 'Mammy' when I was little but she had repressed that of late, saying it was what Irish peasants used; meaning Father.

"Talking? Can it wait, James? The driver is coming in fifty minutes and I am so woefully prepared."

"It's about school, Mama. There's ... there's a new school setting up in the autumn and I'd rather like to go."

"We don't have extra money for fees, James. At your age, you wouldn't realise just how much schooling costs. Schools are not cheap. They have to pay their staff, and all their overheads; the buildings, equipment, utilities and so on. Wherever you go, it must cost only a frugal amount. Who will be running the place?"

Should I lie or go for the knockout blow straight away? Did I mention that I'd seen Ross; that we'd be closely working together? That my mother's former lover was now a part of my life too?

I decided to go for an omission at first and see where it went.

"Actually, Mama, the fees will be very low, very low indeed. In fact, you could say we won't need to pay."

"Oh, how so?"

"It's a friend of mine who's parents are involved in running the school." So far, so honest. "I'm helping them out in return for the fees." (I hadn't thought about it but Douggie and I might have to teach the squeakers if we couldn't recruit a team of MOBsters, so it might not be a complete lie.)

"So you'll be a pupil teacher then?"

"Yes, it looks that way."

"Marvellous." Mama's attention was directed exclusively to her mirror again.

I would tell my friends and those who asked about my mother that she was effusive about Claremont and fully supportive of it. The truth was that she never once visited the place or asked much more ever about it. I think that suited me just fine. In stories about children who go on madcap adventures, the parents are always out of the scene, or the children are orphans. I didn't feel later on that I had been far off either. Perhaps that was why I needed to create my own world – my existing one wasn't really much cop.

As I wandered out of the bedroom, my mother failed to notice. It was clear my birthday was going to be non-existent once more.

I would have to make my own entertainment.

Lesson 7
Careers Guidance

Hove, 1925

Now my mother was about as on board as I was willing for her to be at this point, my next task would be recruiting MOB as the headmaster. I reckoned we'd need a French master eventually as I knew neither MOB nor any of the other teachers I was hoping to poach, could teach it. That wasn't a priority, though, for the moment – MOB could teach a fair few subjects. Science was another subject we'd need someone for and a matron would be required for heath, welfare and cooking.

Despite the early evening drawing in, I reckoned I could kill two birds with one stone and poach MOB and his wife for headmaster and matron. Only problem was, it meant turning up to Holland House which was where the O'Byrnes had rooms. That meant possibly explaining to Clovis Chubb why I was returning to school when I wasn't a boarder and also the Whitsun holidays had now begun. I had started to become a believer in the theory of 'get stuck in and see what happens' so I knew that if I didn't have a plan when I arrived in Cromwell Road, I soon would have.

I rang the doorbell of no 35 and stepped back. It

may have been that the school was empty but I was a young tyke of 11 years old and ringing ahead wasn't the sort of thing young men my age did back then.

"Yeass?" One of the domestic staff opened the door. Her name was Dorothy and she was always kind to us boys, no matter how cheeky we were. She stooped and used her mop as a kind of walking stick. I was never sure if she was just thorough at cleaning or needed constant support.

"Evening Dorothy. Mr O'Byrne is giving me some extra cramming for my scholarship entrance exam."

"Very good, young sir. I'll show you up."

I had never been up onto the top floors of Holland House before and never really wished to again. Dorothy gestured to a door facing a window looking onto the houses behind the school that swept up to the Downs beyond. The evening had firm hold now and the last vestiges of the setting sun were ebbing away. I would be twelve when it next appeared.

Rapping assertively on the door, a voice distantly responded. Footsteps gained in volume and a tired but youthful looking dark-haired woman opened the door. "Hello!" she cheerfully barked. I remember thinking, she must be taller than MOB.

"Eileen O'Byrne at your service, young man. What can I do for you? You'll be after Mick I guess?" Her voice was firm, but had a songbird lilt to it that made me think she sang whenever she could. She was looking down at me with her six-foot frame and making me realise just how small I was back then. Adolescence had yet to make its mark on me. Of course you must be tall, I thought, MOB said your son was six foot tall already. She was the same height as Chubb's horrific mother, but the opposite in personality: warm, welcoming and serene.

As if my thoughts had summoned him up, a tall and gangly adolescent with small round glasses was suddenly looming around the door. He had Mick's hairline, but with a much more generous helping of hair. He looked a mix of youth, health and confidence. "Hullo there!" he said, "Who are you then?"

"James Clifton," I said, answering the boy's question rather than his mother's. "I was after Mr. O'Byrne, but I wonder if I could talk to you both too?" Now I'd responded to both questions.

"Unusual request," said the tall boy, extending his hand in friendship. "I'm William. Bill. I rather like unusual requests, so I guess you'd better come in – do you agree, Mother?"

WOB, I said to myself. *William O'Byrne*. Eileen O'Byrne gestured me into their sitting room.

"Would you be liking a lemonade on this spring evening, Master Clifton?"

"I would. Many thanks."

"My father is not here at the moment, but I can pass on a message if you like?" said WOB. "I've only just got back from boarding school myself so I need to go and see him at ... at his friend's."

"Erm, it's a bit tricky. I need to speak to him, really."

"What's it about, James?" Eileen OB put an opaque and lemony glass in my hand.

Lie, direct, or wait? I decided direct was the best approach. If I was lucky, I would need to work with these people.

"I'm leaving Holland House in the summer for my last year of prep," I said. "This might sound a tad odd, but I'm currently recruiting staff for a new prep school I'm setting up in Second Avenue, which I'll be going to, along with some other boys. We're still short of some teachers and a matron. I... I wondered if Mr O'Byrne might consider..."

Eileen stopped me. "It's very flattering James, but Mick is very happy where he is and he wouldn't want to risk his career by moving from a respectable school to one that's run by one of his pupils."

My mouth was agape. I had thought MOB hated the place too. I decided to fill said mouth with sound. "It's not just me. We have financial backing from the Paynes and a local investor has come on board who is very wealthy. We have a property and boys lined up already for September."

Eileen was looking at me directly. "Do you mean you and Douglas Payne are poaching pupils already from Holland House? You have the nerve to come here, in our holidays, to tell us you are taking funding away from this very institution you are sitting in? We've welcomed you in and you..."

My ears were red and my heart was oscillating like a fan, it felt. My teeth were feeling shaky down to their roots and the pit of my stomach started to squirm.

"Mother, stop!" said WOB, smiling. *He was smiling*?

"You've pulled his leg enough; the poor fellow looks terrified!"

Pulled his leg?

Eileen's face softened and a smile broke out. "Oh, James, your face was priceless then! I can see why Mick talks about you and Douglas. He always said you'd do something like this one day. Marked out for greatness, he always says of you."

My heart returned to its usual place and speed. More or less.

"Mick has been looking for a new post and promotion for a while now. This will be exactly what he needs. Bill, go to the Palmeira and fetch him back. Tell him I don't care if he's just started playing cards. We need to toast an exciting new opportunity! And with you, Bill, looking to go into teaching too!"

WOB grabbed a coat and started to make a bolt for the door. He paused as he was exiting.

"Who are you thinking of as headmaster, James?"

"Well, Mi... Mr O'Byrne actually."

"God help us all!" he grinned and pulled the door behind him.

My birthday, May 30 1925, was on a Saturday that year. My mother had already signed a letter to say I was withdrawing from Holland House. She didn't realise; I slipped a letter I had typed under her nose in amongst her breakfast time correspondence she never paid much attention to until midday and then only gave cursory glances to. I considered it my birthday present to myself as I got a delivery boy to take it to Chubb.

I may not have had a party planned – but I was to have a gathering of sorts. Willett had said we could have the key for the Claremont and Josie Payne had signed the lease on the building for three months, so it seemed a good time to invite the OBs and Ross over that afternoon to see the place. Eileen was interested in the Matron post with all the different roles that would involve and WOB was even considering being our third teacher when old enough. It would seem that I may have lacked my own family these days, but I was acquiring other peoples' at a rate of knots. Claremont was becoming not only a family business, but a family of sorts too.

A school should be more than a school. It *should* be a family. Families have their ups and downs, the off days and on days. But, like all families, it should be where we all grow up together. Whatever age we are. We don't usually choose members of our families in life, but we have to make the best of those we've got around us. As we gathered on that Saturday afternoon, I was starting to realise that I was actually able to have the rare privilege of choosing my family and that this family would then lead me on the path my life was to take.

Josie and Alexander Payne were the last to close the Claremont's substantial door behind them. The Claremont very quickly went from being someone else's previous home to ours. The former owners had fortunately left a lot of their possessions as they apparently were in a hurry to locate overseas. We soon got the lights on and Eileen OB discovered a gramophone under a dust sheet, which was soon playing. As everyone walked around, each imagining what the school would be like, MOB managed to find a drinks cupboard and the adults were soon quaffing sherry whilst we children made do happily with elderflower cordial.

I found MOB in the study at the rear of the house. He was evidently imagining what it would look like with his books and notes in.

"Let's get this right then, Clifton." He rubbed his forefinger sideways across his moustache, which was what he tended to do when he was contemplating. "We've got this place from September, you've got funding and yer want me to be... yer headmaster?"

"Yes."

I tried to look grave and thoughtful and pulled myself up to my full five foot three. Mick had listened the previous night, nodded a lot, but hadn't said much.

"What I don't get, though, is why me. Last time I saw yer before the holidays, I remember I threw a book at yer. Is this mullarkey some type o' strange revenge?"

I laughed and explained that it was actually the blow to the head that got me thinking about setting up the Claremont.

"The big question, young Clifton, is firstly, who is in charge then. Is it me or you?"

"I'd like a say in lessons we teach, Sir, and what the

school is like, but then I'm only here for a year. My scholarship exams are at Christmas. You'll be in charge – it'll be your business, I suppose. I'd just like ... a say."

Mick took off his glasses and looked at me. His eyes, that had seen two years of bullets, shells, explosions, death and shrapnel, looked so tired. The eyes are a window to the soul, it is often said, and Mick's eyes only gave the merest hint of what he'd been through and seen in his forty-odd years. That generation was a decade older than its years.

"A say ... is good. We'd better lose the 'Sir' then outside o' Holland House. If yer a partner in this 'ere school, it'll be 'Mick' from now on - out of earshot of the other buggers, o' course. What subjects should we teach, or not teach then?"

"Everything except Latin. And science should have prominence."

"And what do you want from me in this arrangement? Chubb doesn't pay a fortune, y' know? I haven't pots o' money to invest. My teacher's salary an' army pension mean I can joost about stomp up the lolly t' send Bill to school."

"I just need a headmaster. Someone to lead, teach a bit and be the ... figurehead."

"I think ... I can manage that. If oim to run a school though, sport must play a big role. That mammy's boy Chubb doesn't let yer boys play enough sport and it makes yer brains go to mush."

"Quite." We were strongly agreed on that. "One other thing?"

MOB leaned forward in the swivel chair he had taken a fancy to. "Yes?"

"I think we should avoid meat. I can't stand the stuff. I reckon we should get the boys to eat all types of vegetables and try new recipes that don't involve the killing of animals."

"Yer'll 'ave to talk to Eileen about that. It's never wise to interfere in the workings of the kitchen, I've always found. That's a woman's domain and one me Eileen is very precious about. She's a big woman, young Clifton, you wouldn't want to see 'er when she's got a bee in her bonnet."

He spun slightly around and looked out the window over the garden. "Are you sure I'm the right man for the job, James? I was looking for a new job, but not a headmastership. I'm not really yer man for paperwork and pen pushing."

"I'd be keen to help initially, and you've got your family behind you. There's Ross too." They had met earlier and seemed to hit it off, Mick being a keen golfer and Ross enjoying his cricket so they had much to share. The similarities in looks between the two was uncanny. It would be a strong partnership between the leading funder and Mick as Head.

"How many pupils do you reckon we could get?"

"Payne will be up for it, along with Turle, Hugill and Hall. Then we need a class of younger boys at least to start. Douglas and I will go and visit some younger brothers and perhaps you and Bill could go to some pre-preps to give talks?"

Mick nodded. "I can teach yer maths of course,

English, some French and ancient Greek, but we'll need a swimming teacher. Neither Bill nor I can swim." I had a brainwave – my mother had known an actor in her early career who, I remember she said, loved swimming.

"I know just the man."

"In that case, Mr Clifton, let us go and join our merry gang in what will be, I reckon, the heart of the school." We crossed the hallway and joined the others who were now sat cross-legged on the floor. The music was playing and a couple of hampers had been brought out; Josie Payne had been busy. Champagne was brought out and opened and I must say I enjoyed the taste but found it wasn't something I'd try again. I looked around as Douggie and his family started up the singing. It was an American tune by Vincent Lopez and it was called 'I want to be happy'. They had picked it up recently and it seemed to suit the afternoon perfectly. I realised that I had wanted to be happy for a long, long time and now, today on my birthday, by crikey, it seemed that I actually was.

Clovis Chubb was less happy with the news that two of his pupils and one of his teachers were leaving however, which I was about to discover on the first day back after Whitsun holiday.

Lesson 8
Registration and Junior Assembly

Hove, 1925

"Clifton! My office immediately!" Clovis Chubb was waiting on the steps of Holland House and looked like a fire was brewing inside him. There was sweat trickling down the side of his face on this warm June morning and his badly-fitting toupee was slightly bedraggled and skew-wiff.

He had drawn himself up to his full five-foot-one height and stood behind him was his mother, Mrs Chubb, who weighed in at twenty-one stone and six-foot one. The difference in height made them look as if she should be taking him to school. We had always joked that Clovis Chubb had been found by her from outside the Palmeira.

Poor old Clovis Chubb was left outside a pub
In a basket by his mother
Mummy Chubb had to leave her grub
And bring up the child of another

That was what we used to sing when he wasn't listening and when Mummy Chubb was definitely not around. Whereas he struggled to control us, Mrs

Chubb filled us with fear and was always ready to clip you round the ear. I was sure I could expect a clip around the ear or possibly more over the last few months of my time at Holland House. I would be right.

Chubb gestured roughly that I was to enter his office when we approached the door. I was expecting him to shout at me the moment I entered with all guns blazing. He had a thin and reedy voice that still sounded as if he was approaching adolescence at times and, matched with an inability to pronounce his Rs without adding a 'w' before them, made tellings-off by him less than fearful. As for Mother Chubb however ...

"Sit down, Clifton." He himself sat down in a low back leather chair with curved arms, raised as high off the ground as possible. It reminded me of a small red onion giving him an embrace. We had always wondered whether his feet could touch the ground on his side but no one had ever been that side of the desk when he called them in for a remonstration or the cane. Mother Chubb had now entered too and was standing menacingly behind him, like a huge iceberg looming down on a small lifeboat.

"See to him, Clovis, see to him." Mother Chubb's position veered between cracking her knuckles and folding her meaty arms so tightly she looked as if she was giving a bear hug to an invisible man. She had a tendency to wear stripes which reminded me of cross-section diagrams of large hillsides in geography.

"Mother, calm yourself." Clovis Chubb tried to reassert his authority but his reedy voice was cracking and frayed. "Now, Clifton, you may not know this, but I served in the Great War."

I had always assumed he had played some sort of role, as it was unusual for most men of his age to have done otherwise. I was only five when the war finished and my early years were empty of men; it seemed the country was one big island of women.

"I was a captain, Clifton, just as I am here, of sorts, and as a young man I risked my life many times in that war. In the Royal Army Medical Corps, I sometimes came thirty, no even twenty miles, near to the front line. My ambulance barge of No.1 Ambulance flotilla sailed up to the casualty clearing stations at least once a week and would bring back many wounded men."

His left eye twitched slightly and he gestured to some remembered waterway. "The nurses and orderlies under my control knew that I was not a man to be trifled with." It came out as 'twifled'. "I took no lip from any of the wounded. I said to myself, Clovis, even if a man is in pain, he must still show my wrank some wrespect. One man, after the battle of Arras, whose bullet in his knee was causing him gwief, failed to call me Sir and I had him wait for a bumpy horse drawn ambulance." He let out a slight snort.

"I don't see..." I said, offering a bewildered look. Really though, I knew where this was going.

"What my point is, Clifton, is that Holland House is my ship, much like my ambulance barge in the war. I am in charge, and the orderlies and nurses are the staff. You are the patients, taken from ignorance to a knowledge-filled future at your future school. My wrank here is headmaster and I will tolerwrate no, mark me, no insubordination."

"Sir, I don't get..."

"Insubordination, Clifton is you, setting up your own barge. It is you, diswrespecting my wrank! You, a mere lad still in shorts, think you can run your own set up, and what is worse, take my nurses and orderlies with you! Do you understand me? Nurses and orderlies!"

"Nurses and orderlies," I repeated.

"And what is worse, patients, too. What did I just say, boy? Wrepeat after me: nurses, orderlies and patients." His eye was really twitching by now; fluttering like the wing of a moth.

"Nurses, orderlies and patients," I repeated as ordered.

"You may be stealing O'Byrne from me, and Payne, Hugill and Turle, but it is you who will be on the horse drawn ambulance. You, sir! A horse. Dwawn. Ambulance! He smacked the cane that was on his desk onto its leather surface as he spat out each word. "You will bend over the desk, Clifton."

I was, I must admit a tad scared by now. I had always managed to avoid the cane as my crimes usually involved gazing out of the window at worst.

"Sir, you can't cane me for joining another school, or setting up one for that matter!" I protested. "There's nothing in any school rules that says that is wrong."

"Ahah, Clifton!" Mummy Chubb spoke up, her

gravelly voice resonating around the room. This isn't for that. But you were guilty of breaking two school rules before Whitsun holiday. You not only were inattentive in one of Mr O'Byrne's lessons, but you committed a heinous crime. YOU DAMAGED SCHOOL PROPERTY!"

"How?" I asked.

"HOW?" Chubb Mater bellowed, grabbing me, pulling my hands behind my back and bending me roughly over Clovis' desk. "You ... dared to damage a valuable maths textbook ... with your head!" The Chubbs were now both laughing demonically, cackling and guffawing; a bead of spittle dribbled from Clovis' mouth and Mother Chubb's eyebrows were raised skywards.

"You will learn what happens to those who damage the property of my school, let alone the theft of nurses, orderlies and patients!" Clovis squeaked.

"Repeat after me: nurses, orderlies, patients!"

"Nurses!" THWACK! The cane swished down against my buttocks.

"Orderlies!" THWACK!

"Patients!" THWACK.

I was determined not to yell out but already was feeling pain unlike any I'd ever experienced, except for having a tooth out when I was eight.

"Nurses! Orderlies! Patients!" Again, three more strikes of the cane sent shockwaves of pain deep into my bottom which resonated across my body.

"Now: You are on the Horse! Dwawn! Ambulance! Wepeat those words!".

My backside was already agony. I decided to get my own back. I channelled all my pain and discomfort into shouting out those words, rather than screaming in pain. Years of dull lessons, clips around the ear and most of all those bloody horrible plates of beef – I vented all my anger from those and the sheer injustice of it all into shouting those words. It may get me a raw backside I'd not be able to sit down on for weeks, but I would shout those words so everyone in the assembly taking place just then could hear – and I'd say it exactly as Chubb asked...

"HORSE!" WHACK!

"DWAWN!" WHACK!

"AMBULANCE!"

No WHACK this time.

"You mock me, boy? You will wepeat these words ten times more!"

"WEPEAT THESE WORDS TEN TIMES MORE!"

WHACK! WHACK! WHACK!

"Not those words. Wepeat these words!"

"WEPEAT THESE WORDS!"

WHACK! WHACK! WHACK! WHACK! WHACK!

"Horse dwawn ambulance!"

"HORSE DWAWN AMBULANCE!"

"No! By God, Clifton, you will wespect my wrank!"

"I WILL WESPECT YOUR WRANK! AND YOUR HORSE DWAWN AMBULANCE!"

MOB was leading assembly when the Chubbs marched me in. I think I had had a further twenty-seven lashes of the cane by that time, including one which hit my coccyx. But, by jove, it had been worth it. The seventy-four boys of Holland House were all staring at me in amazement, and were trying their hardest at stifling giggles.

"Boys!" MOB called, and they turned towards him. "All stand for the headmaster."

Chubb took his place on the stage. "We will forego the school song and our hymn today."

He scowled. "As you may have heard, some of our senior boys are planning to leave us this year, even though this school has nurtured, cared for and educated them. And in the year they will need our staff for maximum assistance with their scholarship applications. One of our ship's crew has decided to disloyally depart as well, and leave us for an amateur establishment that will last half a year at most." Here he looked at MOB.

"So I say to you, boys, as tempting as it may be to go and join a school set up by a boy whose head is full of wool, of dweams and of arrogance, wemember that here at Holland House, you have a real school, that has been awound for sevewal decades and will go on for many more."

With a swish of his cape, he spun around and marched out of the hall, Mummy Chubb following. I felt dozens of eyes gazing at me and then MOB continued with the assembly. I wondered what he would say and hoped he wouldn't sit everyone down as I wasn't sure what noise I would make when my bottom made contact with the wooden floor.

"Boys, we are gathered today to remember that life is SHORT." MOB definitely put emphasis on the last words, or was I imagining it? All of us here on MOTHER Earth are here to do good and to make the most of our SHORT lives." There he was, doing it again!

"I want to let you know that whatever RANK you are in society," He mouthed the word loudly but carefully. "Adults have nothing but RESPECT for you and will always try to prepare you for whatever job you go on to do; whether you work with HORSES or with AMBULANCES." The grin was evident on his face now. MOB was thoroughly enjoying himself. The boys were starting to laugh also at the gamut of digs at Chubb.

"Now, I want you to all remember never to NURSE a grudge against anyone who has done you wrong and always demonstrate PATIENCE with those less tolerant with you." The boys were now laughing loudly, wondering what message MOB would send last of all to Chubb.

"Gentlemen, starting with the seniors, I'd like you to file out of the assembly hall now in an ORDERLY way and always remember not to BARGE anyone out of the way."

The boys left the hall in shrieks of laughter.

For the rest of the term the Chubbs were on the lookout for anything MOB or I did wrong. Douggie also found himself in the head's office once or twice on a trumped-up charge. We never spoke about this to our parents; Douggie, as it would upset his parents, and me, well, my mother wasn't really that concerned with anything outside of her failing music career. MOB and his family left employment with the Chubbs halfway through the summer term and thankfully Josie Payne offered them accommodation free of charge for the last few weeks and throughout the summer until their rooms were ready at Claremont.

It also took the pressure off them so that they could go and start recruiting pupils and parents to Claremont. Jock Hugill, Brian Turle, Douggie and myself were to be the first four senior pupils but we knew we'd need at least ten pupils to make the school work financially in its first year. We decided we would be like a press gang in the Napoleonic wars – we would go and pressurise (nicely) boys to join our ship.

Brian had a tipoff from his younger sister that her friend's brother, Maurice Brigden was looking for a new school and so he was one of the boys that we decided to target.

Brigden was our number 9 target. Douggie was No.1, the Sheriff twins – Ronald & Norman 2 and 3, Antony Chamier No 4, Ronald Simmons No 5, Jock Hugill No 6, and we were waiting to hear if Michael Parnell-Smith and Eric Hall would be joining us in September.

It was early evening in early July when we had arranged with Mr and Mrs Brigden to visit their house in Third Avenue. We'd explained that MOB and his son would be late and asked if they wanted MOB to attend from the start, but they had said that they were happy with just the junior section of the recruitment mob. As we arrived, Maurice, who was seven years old, was gazing down at us from the first floor of their grand house through the bannisters. He was a cheerful-looking, bubbly young chap who we'd vaguely known over the years.

"Good evening, Mr and Mrs Brigden!" Douggie and I were in the new grey flannelette suits we had purchased from Cobleys the outfitters. We had decided the Hove shop would be best to supply the school uniform as it was closest to us. We had polished our black shoes, our belt buckles and our patter. We did not yet have the caps we had ordered. Still, we felt leaving these off gave us the air of youthful salesmen rather than schoolboys and we had practiced our sales pitch several times now.

Eliza and Digby Bridgen shook our hands, welcoming us through and into their parlour. They poured fresh lemonade and sat whilst we stood and presented our spiel. Young Maurice was peeking around the parlour door.

"Mr and Mrs Brigden, and especially Maurice, we are here tonight to invite you to send young Maurice to our exciting new school, Claremont, which opens in September this year."

"Thank you, Douglas. Yes, we believe Maurice will thrive and enjoy himself at our new school, based just two streets away in the plush and luxurious building of Claremont House. Boys will enjoy teaching in one class which we hope will soon become two – one for 7-

9-year olds and one for those of 9-13 years. Lessons will be taught by Mr Michael O'Byrne, his son, William, who has studied at Winchester College and Mr Alec Ross, an experienced sportsman and businessman. For Maurice's fees, he will enjoy lessons by competent and knowledgeable staff, a range of sporting and hobby activities and be encouraged to develop and pursue his own interests."

Maurice wandered out at this point into the parlour. He looked at his parents and then up at us with interest and, possibly, a tad of admiration on his face.

"You can see though, boys, we are a tad nervous about the move," said Mr Brigden. "What you are doing is very admirable, but it is a leap of faith whenever a new school starts up, let alone one that had children, no matter how intelligent, as its 'shareholders'. Why should we take this chance with your Messrs O'Byrne and Ross?"

"Daddy, I'd rather like to go to this school." Maurice looked up at his father. Douglas and James make it sound fun and as if I'll do well there."

"We're not doing this on a whim, Mr Bridgen." Douggie looked at me as he spoke. "We think it's important that Claremont is run by adults, but those who are going to benefit from it get a say; that pupils have a ... voice. All men and nearly all women have a say in how the country is run now; it seems likely all women will have the vote as young as 21 in a year or two. Should children not have a say in how their schools are run?"

"To us," I chipped in, "a school is our country. Its teachers are our politicians, our royalty. The classrooms are our counties; its traditions are our traditions. It is the first organisation we have experience of – should it not matter to us?"

We were not being defensive or hostile, and nor was Mr Brigden. It felt like a grown-up debate on a point and our eloquence and Maurice's positive stance was helping.

"Well, boys," Digby Brigden looked at his wife and they held hands. "You have an experienced teacher, a good home for this school; from your literature we can see boys will be well fed, smartly dressed, cared for and engaged in pursuits that are healthy and wholesome. I think I can say it looks like our Maurrie will be with you in September!"

They weren't all as easy as that. Some parents would only deal with MOB and Eileen, some were loyal to Clovis Chubb and others just keen to go to, or stay at, existing schools. As summer approached we had eight pupils – still two short to make the school anywhere near a working proposition. If this wasn't worrying enough, Douggie and I still had to face our last day at Holland House and whatever surprises Clovis and Mummy Chubb had in store for us.

Lesson 9
Dismissal and Summer Holidays

Hove, 1925

The assembly room, down in the basement of Holland House, was full. Not one child was away on that early July Friday - the last of term. I think they expected, just as we did, that Clovis wasn't going to see his pupils and a teacher depart to a new, rival school without a scene. Especially after MOB's micky-taking of Chubb that day after my caning.

Unbelievably though, Chubb didn't say a word. Not one. But two. As we were dismissed for the holidays, he just looked me in the eye and mouthed two words. *Six months*. That was all he gave us.

I pretty much believed him during that summer as potential parents all seemed to be on holiday. This was the 'roaring twenties', as they came to be known, before the Wall Street Crash and the Great Depression that followed worldwide. For the families that had survived the Great War in some form, this was that period of light between two of darkness. It looked unlikely we would get our two desperately needed pupils until we started and Ross and the Paynes' funding would only last so long without sufficient fees. Financially, unless we took on more pupils the

Claremont would indeed last for about six months and Chubb would be proved right.

If Claremont's future was shaky, my present was the happiest it had ever been that summer. I was firmly ensconced at Douglas's house along with the OBs and had little need to visit my mother, which suited her just fine. One or two days a week we decorated the Claremont and scrounged tables, chairs; whatever we needed. Eileen O'Byrne was busy ordering food and hiring kitchen and domestic staff. She would have a lady called Woodruff and the domestic staff were to be two fellows called Clements and Keeley, who seemed good chaps, and not adverse to having two twelve-year olds as their co-bosses. Between the four of them, there would be a range of tasks to fulfil but that was all the staff we could afford.

MOB had been told by Clovis Chubb that he would do everything in his path to ensure that no boy in the county would go to the school and when Claremont failed, Chubb would ensure he never worked again. His reference would tell no headmaster to employ him. Chubb told MOB that when he came crawling back to him, there would be no job for him at Holland House.

MOB told him to stick his head up his mother's arse and inhale deeply.

This meant the pressure was on. We would have to ensure that Claremont didn't fail and so we had to have a wider range of sports than any other school in the area. One day, sat in the Payne's garden, Josie, the OBs, Douggie and I discussed what would help us achieve this. Josie said that parents sent their children to Brighton and Hove, as it was a seaside resort, so it made sense we mentioned in any literature sea swimming lessons. This reminded me that I had promised Mick I would get him a swimming teacher. Which was why I had to speak to my mother again.

Herbert Marshall was exactly where Mother said he would be on the early August day Douggie and I met him – in the sea. Hove had for many years talked about building a pier to rival Brighton's two and he later told us he would swim in the spot where it had been originally planned, and would do so until it was built. There had been six different sites that been mooted by 1925, but Herbert only swam around the proposed site of the first plan.

Douggie and I perched on one of the groynes near Third Avenue and watched him swim. He would never swim east or west, only out to sea and then back to shore, unaware we were watching him. Later we found out that he was swimming the outline of where he believed the pier in Hove would once be, keen to do it before building started. He was determined it would be built and refused to be told otherwise.

There was something odd about his movement in the water that I couldn't quite put my finger on, though. I remember what my mother had mentioned about Herbert Brough Falcon Marshall, to use his full name. These days he partly worked in a stock company in Brighton but had made his stage debute in 1911, and now Bart, as he was known, was getting increasing amounts of theatrical work around the country and across the Atlantic.

It was rumoured that Hollywood was impressed with his potential back then in 1925, which proved true, as today in 1940 he indeed has a long career in film behind him. He even starred in an Alfred Hitchcock movie back in 1930. The question was, could he fit in the odd swimming lesson in his increasingly busy career? Swimming teachers back then were hard to find.

"Mr Marshall?" I walked down to the gently lapping foam at the sea's edge and called out.

"Halloo!" He stopped swimming, stood up in what was a slightly awkward motion. The water covered the bottom half of his body, but you could clearly see why Hollywood wanted him as a movie star; he had classical good looks. Even rising up from being submerged under the sea, his hair was still neatly parted and his features looked chiselled by a master craftsman.

"Do I know you?"

"My mother, Estelle Clifton, performed with you in Nigel Playfair's repertory troupein *The Younger Generation*?" Marshall's eyes lit up somewhat. Knowing Marshall's reputation today as a ladies' man and my mother's indiscretions, it would be no surprise if they had some sort of alliance. Perhaps once more, my mother's love life would help get my school off the ground,.

"Ah, Estelle, such a dainty and gorgeous flower. You look slightly like her, Master Clifton. I'm not your father by any chance, am I?"

"No, I don't think so, Sir."

"Well, that's one less worry. How can I be of service to you or your delightful mother? Is she well, by the way? I heard she lives nearby." I imagined he had more than heard, but many actors resided in Brighton then and now due to its many opportunities for roles outside of the capital, as well as being a healthy place to be 'resting' between jobs in the West End.

"I'm involved in a business venture, Sir. A school. The headmaster, Mr O'Byrne is looking for a swimming master and I know you're busy but wondered if you'd be keen to help out for a few months whilst we get the school started? Mother said you enjoy your swimming so."

"A part-time job at your age? Very commendable, very commendable indeed, young Master Clifton. She is correct. I do so enjoy the daily battle with the briny. I am resting for a few months before my next role across the Atlantic so your request is timely. I heartily accept. Do you battle with the briny, Master Clifton?"

"Erm ... I do quite like a swim, yes Sir."

"I find it preferable to the other battle I faced back in Arras in 1917. Cost me this." Holding onto the groyne with one hand he hopped forward to reveal his left leg was missing, leaving a small stump starting above where his knee would have been.

"You've only one leg?" My mother had never mentioned his one leg. Or the missing one either, for that matter.

"Well done, Clifton, state the obvious!" Douggie laughed at me, throwing stones into the sea.

"Amazing what one German bullet can do, eh?" He hopped onto the groyne and perched his bottom onto it. "They would have very nearly saved it, the medics, but some tiny little Medical Corps officer on a power trip refused to evacuate me quick enough from the Casualty Clearing Station. Wanted me to call him "Sir" whilst I was howling in pain, would you believe? Refused to let me on the bloody barge!"

"Who would do a thing like that?" asked Douggie.

"Quite. Happy to get the young of today into the briny. Nothing better for a lad. Pass me my leg, would you?" I realised that one of the wooden supports of the groyne had not actually been the groyne at all, but a wooden prosthetic leg, its elastic straps tied around another upwards support.

"Marvellous what they can make these days isn't it?"

He gestured for Douggie to fetch his shirt, tie, shoes, socks and trousers, further up the groyne on a dry section. He rapped it with his knuckles. "George V visited the hospital I was treated in and under a blanket, he guessed the wrong leg was the false one!" He chuckled and his face became friendly as well as handsome. I warmed to him instantly.

A one-legged future Hollywood actor who was also a swimming teacher seemed to suit our madcap school rather well.

Lesson 10
Biology (Domestic Science)
Hove, 1925

Apart from our swimming teacher's actual legs, there was another thing at Claremont we had only one of – a soccer ball.

Eileen O'Byrne, who had now become 'Matron' to all or 'EOB' had miscalculated when placing the initial food order. Rather than 20 tins of braising beef, she had mistakenly written '2,000'. This added to our financial woes and meant our budget ran out. Subsequently, our Physical Ed cupboard just had one borrowed football in it come early September.

EOB was delighted however when the delivery arrived. "Young gentlemen should have beef every day." She smiled, trying to bring light to the delivery men's refusal to return the order. "A young man needs his beef – iron, minerals, health on a plate. It's like Guinness and cigarettes. Good for your stomach, lungs and kidneys. The beef was good for my health in one ruddy way only – I gained bigger muscles lifting and storing the perishing tins which were everywhere that summer.

To escape the near igloo of beef, Douggie and I found a kindly homeowner further down Second Avenue who had a large garden and was willing to let us play sports in it. Jock, Brian, Douggie, Brigden and I had been thoroughly testing it out and had ruddy faces when the final member of 'staff' arrived.

An underfed Alsatian had calmly wandered up the steps to Claremont as MOB was up a ladder, erecting the school's sign with WOB.

It stood there and looked at us.

"Jesus!" said MOB. "It looks like Buelis, the milkman, so it does!"

And it did. It had the same ugly, scrunched up face and leaned its head to one side the same way that Buelis the Milkman did. We never found out who his owner had been and so the dog became the O'Byrne's dog and became known as Buelis. I'm not sure if our milkman ever noticed our comparing him with MOB's Alsatian.

One week later, it stole our only ball and buried it on Hove Lawns. A second one had been rodgered so hard by it that it burst, as had our goalposts (they would never stand up straight again).

By opening day, Buelis had buried EOB's furry hat, MOB's pipe and Bill's harmonica. The last two in the same day. I had lost two caps, a flute and Douggie had lost four socks. We never saw them again and the council were always complaining about Buelis's latest mound of earth on its pristine lawns. Tennis balls were Buelis's greatest love, though. I estimated that by the start of 1926, he had munched his way through at least a dozen. Buelis and I shared one thing in common: he also couldn't face Mrs O'Byrne's mountains of prime tin beef.

Lesson 11
Head Boy's Assembly

Hove, 1925

Talking of animals, it was one thing to get the carcass of a school together; the building, equipment and resources. It is another to get the internal organs in place – its staff. It is also another thing altogether to ingest the body with its diet of juicy seven- and twelve-year-olds however, so – as the first day of term approached – I became increasingly nervy.

By the time Monday September 7 arrived, I was jumpier than a sackful of kittens. Matron saw the state I was in as we were all making final preparations in the basement that morning and put two hands on the sides of my shoulders.

"Bernard." She too had adopted my preferred name, saying that it was an Irish custom anyway to use a boy's second name and, as this school had more than a touch of the Irish about it, it was how we decided we should do things too.

"You've done enough now, so you have. You go up into Room 1 with Mick and I will greet the boys outside."

I did as I was told, checked the coat pegs one last time and climbed the stairs. I looked around and stood up on the platform we had assembly on. It was by the window and we had decided it was our stage for lectures, plays and awards. It wobbled slightly because Mick wasn't the world's best carpenter. He had nailed more nails into himself than the floor or wood when he was building it and I had learnt a few new swearwords I had never heard before.

I climbed down from the rickety stage and looked out of the spotless bay windows. Eileen O'Byrne was indeed standing at the top of the basement stairs, her matron's uniform billowing slightly in the September sea breeze despite copious starching.

What if nobody came? What if they got cold feet? What had I been thinking of? We had no fees paid yet, insufficient children to pay our bills...

"Clifton!"

MOB was standing behind me. He was wearing his new robes and mortar board. He had cleaned up his best suit and his tie was in its usual slightly askew position, which I always attributed to the shakes he exhibited as a result of the war. There was just one bit of corned beef hash smeared just below his left pocket.

"Faces tell tales." He said in a gentle tone. "Yours ... well, it tells me you are regretting what you've done, you are wishing you hadn't started these whole shenanigans off and you don't think anything will happen today. Am I right?"

I turned round to face him. "Is it that obvious? Really?" I knew at that point this man, who seemed to me now to have become something of the father I pined for so greatly, was the right choice for the school. No, he was the school. I had been the acorn, or

I at least had planted it, but he was the head gardener. He, and his wonderful family would water it, protect it, watch it grow and that tree, I knew now, would indeed grow, branch and thrive.

"Sometimes Clifton, when you're at the top of a steep hill ... you just have to let the wheels run. Let them run and run and run."

"Thanks." I croaked, my voice retreating to a whisper mid-word.

A boy on a bike turned the corner of Second Avenue. It was Antony Chamier, quickly followed by the Sheriff twins, both laughing and trying to knock each other off their bikes. Then came Hugill, with Ronald Simmons on his handlebars, then Ronald and Norman, Parnell-Smith, Brigden and his chum, whose name I always forgot, ran across the road from the western side. Lastly, dear old Douggie swept into the road, his satchel swinging wildly to the right as he veered rapidly around the corner at breakneck speed. Even from this distance I could tell he was badly whistling a tune. My heart seemed to fill with a warm liquid, my toes tingling and a huge sense of pride seemed to seep out of every pore of my body. It was happening!

The boys had stopped in a line, facing Mrs OB. Douggie, with another theatrical cycling sweep, pulled in to the front of the line and hopped, with his bike up onto the pavement. He alighted and inspected the boys before joining the front of the queue. Through the open window, I could hear that it all went silent.

Douggie took his cap off to Eileen O'Byrne.

"Good morning, Matron." He said.

"Good morning, Douglas." She replied. "Wheel your bike down the steps, will you now."

"Aye, Marm." The other boys doffed their caps to and followed Douggie.

I could hear shuffling of feet as bags were hung up on hooks and the domestics helped store the bikes away in the small, front basement garden. A quick cup of tea was had by all; I remained upstairs, rehearsing in my head what I wanted to say in that first assembly before we all started our first lesson. The day was to start with algebra, followed by some history, trigonometry, French and ancient Greek. We would read after lunch our first text, and then MOB had games planned with Bill for the afternoon.

We would then return for some tea, afternoon hobbies and music before final lessons and then home. We wouldn't have our first boarder, it had been agreed, until the spring when, hopefully, funds had allowed us to fit out the bedrooms a bit more.

There was a knock at the front door and Mick went to see who it was. We had asked parents not to visit on this first day and that we would have a parents' meeting in the second week. For a second I wondered if it was Chubb, ready to storm in and make a scene. Or even worse, Mater Chubb.

It turned out to be a rather small, Italian man, with a hint of a smell of linoleum about him and a baggy hat, leaning across one eyebrow and over one ear.

"He's been sent, compliments of your mother, so he says." Mick looked slightly amused.

"Hello, James. I am Cantaneo. Your mother, she... she said you need the music to make your school ... alive. We play for your young gentile-men, yes?"

I hadn't thought about having music playing as the boys entered assembly. It seemed a splendid idea to be honest. It was typical of my mother though, not willing or able to put a penny into the school, but willing to make this gesture.

"That would be wonderful, Mr Cantaneo."

"*Belissimo ragazzo*, no?" he said to MOB of me, as he walked back towards the door. "I – ah get my men!"

Two elderly Italian gents shuffled into the hallway, one carrying a cello, and the other, a tiny old man with white curly hair somehow managed to bring in a harp that was bigger than he was. Cantaneo himself reached into the doorway and picked up a barrel organ. After some preliminary squeaks, strums and coughs they set up in the corner of Room 1 and began to play. The sound of Puccini reverberated throughout the Victorian house.

Eileen O'Byrne was matronly marching the boys, now well fed and watered, up the stairs. MOB and I had decided to give the stage a miss, mainly as we weren't sure whether it would take our combined weights. We stood in front of it, hands behind backs. I gripped the back of my grey flannel suit and twisted it tightly for comfort. The first words ever spoken at Claremont School were about to be said to its first ever pupils.

The boys came in, without their caps on and sat

down, cross-legged in two rows. Brigden and his chum were in the first row and the older boys sat behind. We had agreed we were to all be taught as one class until we got a few more boys and then we would split into juniors and seniors.

"Thank you, gentlemen." MOB gestured to Cantaneo and his men and they rested their instruments.

"Welcome to Claremont School boys, on its very first ever day. Some of you will know me, and my name is Mr Michael O'Byrne.

You are the first, we hope, of many pupils who will walk up those stairs, learn your lessons, increase your knowledge and bloom into decent, and more importantly, interesting young men." He dabbed at the bushiest part of his moustache.

"Beginnings are where we start. They are where we lay down our rules and make up our traditions. My rules are simple and will not be enforced by the cane. Nor will they be followed by throwing of objects at you. I heard some silly bugger did that to a boy somewhere near here and all sorts of stupidity followed." The boys and I laughed. Mick smiled.

"Rule the first. Do no harm, keep only kindness in your mind. I've seen mankind doing its worst to each other in the fields of Flanders, and so I want you to eradicate even the smallest of nasty gestures from your actions. What the world needs now, so it does, when we have millions underground across the channel still rotting away,, is friends, neighbours and allies, not enemies and so I will not have boys not getting along. This school will be for any boy of any nation, of any race, creed and colour."

"Rule two. Try new things. Attempt, not contempt is what I want. And thirdly, no snobbery, or looking down on your fellow man. The boy next to you is not the sum of what his parents earn, not what he can afford to pay, not a reflection of the bank balance his family have. He is a human being, the most amazing creation on God's green earth. A perfectly balanced machine of thought, precision, sinews, talent, creativeness and calculation. He may well be the man in ten, fifteen, twenty years who flies across the Pacific, drives at two hundred miles an hour, climbs Everest or bowls for England. Intellectual snobbery is fine, though – we'll definitely look down at those too daft to leave Holland House!" We all chuckled at this.

"Lastly. My family come from a long line of Irish aristocrats in Wicklow, a grand place in the south-east of Ireland. Our motto is *Certavi et vici*, which means *I have fought and I conquered*. The only place I want you lot fighting and conquering is on the rugby field and the cricket pitch. So, most of all: let's play lots of good cricket and have some *fun*."

The boys cheered at the last one.

"I don't think I need to introduce James Clifton here. Is there anything you'll be saying, young man?"

My mouth went dry. I have spoken in boardrooms since then, to people in different countries and of all ages, but that September morning was the toughest ever. Keep it short, stupid, I said to myself. People remember a balls-up.

"Only thank you, from the bottom of my heart, for choosing Claremont. We've all, most of us, been to a school we hated. Here we have a chance to build the school we love. And one I hope year after year of boys will go on to love, too. Thank you for being the founding fathers of Claremont. I hope one day we will tell our children and grandchildren of this day. Enjoy your lessons today."

They only went and ruddy clapped me!

Bill then entered the room. He had a look on his face I only ever saw once again; it was when he made his one and only first-class appearance for Sussex, playing against Cambridge University at the County Cricket Ground in 1935. I made a special journey back just to see him, but was too shy, for once, to make a move and see him afterwards. In Sussex's first innings on that day, he was dismissed for 8 runs. In their second innings, he was caught out after only 26 runs and his batting average was only 17.00 but he just had this look of ... belonging. On both occasions, his whole posture just said *this is where I'm meant to be*. The match was his only major appearance for Sussex, but his speech that day as a sixteen-year-old, would be incredibly prophetic in hindsight.

"Boys, I'm not going to speak long, but I wanted to introduce myself as one of your teachers."

"Hi Bill!" said Jock and Douggie. As MOB's son, when not away at school, he had always been around Holland House and so they all knew him well, despite his being five years older than the oldest Claremont boys.

"Hi," Bill smiled. "For those new lads, as you may have worked out, my name is William O'Byrne, and I'll be teaching you ... well, anything my father doesn't. And cricket too, when he lets me."

This raised a laugh or two. "But more importantly, I heard the words a certain other headmaster said about my father, our senior partner here (he pointed at me) and our chances at this school. Let me say this: he can say what he likes. Claremont is not just a flash in the pan. We will be here for a long, long, time, no matter what the world has to throw at us, especially if I have anything to do with it. Claremont is here to stay!"

This hit the spot and gained the biggest cheer yet.

Mick then ordered everyone into two groups – the young ones with Bill for maths and us lot with him. The first maths task we did made me laugh and worry at the same time. It was the costs of running a school against ten pupils paying fees and how many pupils the school would need to break even.

The first day went well and we even managed a walk down to the house down the sea end of Second Avenue, where we had a small game of rounders and cricket. Four days later, Mick and Bill were needed to go and meet a parent about a much-needed prospective pupil. Alec Ross took the older lads for geography and I was left with the seven-year olds for maths. Eileen O'Byrne would be there to pop in occasionally to see I hadn't killed anyone in amongst cooking the beef casserole she was massacring for lunch. I set them a task based on engineering that Mick had set me a year or two back.

There was a bit of giggling, much as Bill had got from us older ones, with boys trying to keep a straight face when they called me 'sir' or 'Mr Clifton'. I tried not to giggle when they kept pretending to be daydreaming to try and get me to throw a book at them.

During lunch that day, boys kept coming into the dining hall and running off to the toilet to be sick. Eileen was worried it was her cooking, but it turned out that the younger boys had discovered that the house had three taps in its bathrooms from its day as a luxury villa. Like a number of other Hove houses of that size and prestige, it had seawater pumped into its bathrooms, and the boys had started drinking the mottled and musty seawater for dares.

I was very glad when MOB and WOB returned. Even more glad when they revealed that they had not just one, but two new boys starting in a few weeks' time.

Lesson 12
Physical Education

Hove, 1925

"The secret of a good school," Bill confided to me over breakfast one morning, "I reckon,, is to help every boy find something he is good at, let him know he is good at it, and let him know you know it too."

This was proving to be harder than we thought.

Our first PE lessons showed that we had a group of especially inept young sportsmen. We were looking very unlikely to be a school renowned for any sport, something that would be important for us to attract the remaining needed students. Cricket, to MOB and WOB's utter dismay, proved to be a source of terrible slapstick rather than cricketing excellence. Nor was it helped that Buelis, Mick's adopted ugly Alsatian insisted on following us to the County Cricket Ground and on stealing our one and only cricket ball.

He then made himself very happy continuing to repeat this trick with our rugger, footie and tennis balls. Lacross sticks ended up being buried after being gnawed and he did something unmentionable to Mick's cricket pads that made Eileen scream and call him a 'great, dirty, heathen brute.' The smile on his great ugly gargoyle of a face was a sight to see, though. That dog knew exactly what he was doing and loved every minute of it; especially when Mick swore repeatedly at him.

Marshall's swimming lessons were a great success, but he was unaware that, when he asked boys to copy his technique, they only used one leg, too. The sight of a dozen pupils only kicking right legs and hence swimming round in circles made us probably look more like a synchronised swimming team than a precise body of potential Olympic swimmers, which is what we wanted.

Alec Ross looks incredibly narked in every photo you see of him, looking distantly off to his right. This was his look of despair, as we called it after his attempts to teach us the game that he was playing for Scotland on an international level. He would be away, still, for weeks at a time during 1925 and 1926 as he went to win the Swiss Open both those years (he had won it first in 1923) and both times he came back, we celebrated his victory and then his determination to pass on his success slowly ebbed away again. No wonder he didn't stay for long and returned to America about the time I, too, moved on.

Cross country wasn't too bad, we were glad to discover. In Jock Hugill, Parnell-Smith and one of the new boys, Lowe, we had a trio with real dedication, pace and stamina. The only problem was, these three were also our worst at geography, map-reading, following directions or even point-blank listening, so consequentially, they all got lost running around Hove. Lowe ended up in Rottingdean, quite a few miles east of Brighton and we only recovered him when the police called us and asked if we were missing one of our runners. We eventually solved this problem by getting parents involved, who had homes and businesses around the area. Spread around the course of the streets and the promenade and using several cars they would drop cut up paper in front of the boys so we had a paperchase to follow.

This worked really well until one poor couple had a mid-week wedding in Hove and all the confetti led to Jock ending up running up the aisle of Hove Methodist church and disturbing the ceremony. There were a lot of confused wedding guests wondering why an 11-year old in running gear was following the bride up the aisle.

Sailing was equally farcical. We chartered two sailing dinghies from the local sailing club and were wondering why,, despite our best efforts,, our races seemed not to be very competitive. It transpired both boats were caught up in the marker buoy for the West Pier and we were trying to tow that along. We gave up after that and went back to swimming around in circles in the sea instead until it got too cold as autumn's colder grip tightened.

Lesson 13
Staff Meeting

Hove, Winter 1925

By November, we finally gave up on our lengthened cricket season. MOB continued to get us to challenge other schools to matches throughout October in the vain hope that we would show some potential to beat some school; any school. It was hopeless, though: we couldn't bat, bowl or run, on the whole, and the ability to catch someone out from another school was beyond most of the team. We had a keen cricketer in MOB and Bill would go on to be a county cricketer. If your ingredients for a steak and kidney pie aren't of the finest quality, it won't taste of much, as Eileen used to say.

Speaking of Bill, he was taking more lessons and so we felt able to split the class into two. From now on, the juniors would be the 7-9 year olds and the 10-13 year olds were to be prepared for the few scholarships and the other places to public schools separately. With three more boys coming on board, MOB felt happy enough at last to employ more teachers. We now had Messrs Sharpe and Poynter, who were part time, as well as a temporary teacher, Mr Horobin.

These three were all rather quiet characters compared with MOB, but then anyone would have been, to be honest. He had always been mercurial in nature and temperament, but his mood swings seemed more pronounced now. Sometimes his lessons went by with him not much more than whispering, whereas at other times he was his usual animated, magnetic self, all arms and limbs waving, but this could also lead to his temper erupting, which worried me as I now was seeing a new side to him. He didn't seem completely in control of this side of his personality anymore and I was concerned that the odd clip round the ear, volley of shouts or cuff of the head would lead to pupils leaving or new ones not joining.

It was strange seeing the school not as a consumer, as I had been before, but as a manager and director, of sorts. Every boy was not just a soul to be taught, developed, nurtured and cared for, but a sum of money essential for paying for wages, electricity, rent, resources, food, maintenance and a hundred other things.

Bill seemed to have aged ten years in two months. Gone was the gangly youth, the thinner, more youthful version of his father, who walked around with the bouncing stomp that young men of his age and gait seemed to have. He walked now with a slight stoop and had taken on much of the administrative work from his father, as MOB denounced paperwork as 'sheets of the shite o' the devil'.

Bill seemed more worried about his father than I was, which of course was natural, as MOB was his father, but there was evidently something Bill knew that we didn't. I didn't realise at that time, but Bill later explained that it was flashbacks from the war. MOB saw each piece of paper put in front of him when he was going through a flashback, as an order from Battalion HQ ordering him and his men to advance again into no man's land. You could see why he didn't write a single thing down in his time as head. Bill told me it had taken seventeen hours lying in no man's land before stretcher bearers made it to him to get him back to the Regimental Aid Post. He saw one group of four men, sent to retrieve him, blown to pieces by one shell and couldn't move all that time; his knee in tatters and blood ebbing from him all that time deep into the lethal mud of Flanders.

And what was the effect of the school on me? I realised, as I sat down one night in one of the upper bedrooms I had adopted in Claremont as my other home and study, writing my own school report, that I was in a unique position; one that no other boy or girl would undertake, possibly ever again. I had a sense of realisation that things could be achieved in this life if we put our minds to it.

I was determined to get a scholarship and the place I had my eye on was Herne Bay, where Douggie's father had offered to put me up in their other home. After living in Hove, I just couldn't move away from the sea but also the school there had a good track record of getting their boys into the Navy, which I rather fancied. I was determined to follow MOB in his original career, that of engineer. I had made a school, now I wanted to make and build other things. It also felt like the nearest thing I had to a family business.

On that thought, it made me realise that the man I worried about more than my real father, MOB, was family. I also realised therefore that family is not who just who you are related to; it's who you relate to.

As we sat formally together in the garden on an unseasonably warm December morning one Friday in the garden at No. 13, I realised there were actually thirteen boys now in all present that day, matching the number of the house. It seemed to have some sort of neat symmetry, as if we'd met some sort of target I hadn't realised existed until that moment.

Douggie was there grinning away, as was I, the first time you could see me clearly in a photo - in the first ever one with Ross teaching us golf, my face is in darkness, and all you can see are my ears sticking out. I was sat to the right of Eileen O'Byrne, her face smiling as she planned how much gelatinous beef she was going to insert into us that lunchtime. MOB, dead centre of the photo, looks slightly like an elderly Hitler in this picture and is gazing intently at the camera. Simmonds, shooting above us at the back, looks far older than his twelve years in the picture. I remember staring at his top lip and being fascinated that he had a sprouting of dark hairs protruding from it when I looked around, before the photographer made us all sit still.

The photo was also the first time we were all captured in our school uniform that I had chosen. In the golfing photo with Ross, a few chaps were wearing their old school uniforms or suits they had borrowed for school. The December shot, with the garden all bare except for the ivy clinging to the garden wall behind, was the first time I really believed we could make it, and as Bill had said, that Claremont was here to stay.

You can see how he has suddenly become a young man, with responsibilities beyond that which most men of his age had in this photo. He was partly responsible for the future of over a dozen boys. He would soon have much more responsibility that he realised.

Lesson 14
History

Hove, 1926

On the same February day Douggie's failure to catch Belmont School's best batter out cost us another match, I was away at the Old Ship Hotel in Brighton sitting my scholarship exam for Herne Bay. I must admit, I felt I had similarly fluffed it, and missed a catch (academically speaking). The question on the Peloponnesian War I felt I had answered correctly, but only if you view 'correctly' as meaning answering the question you wanted to answer, not the one you were actually being asked.

If I failed the scholarship exam, Mother had made it quite clear that funds for Master James Bernard McCarthy Clifton Esquire were non-existent and my options were limited. I wasn't entirely sure if she would make me start a trade, but it was a possibility. My dreams of living with the Paynes and engineering in the Royal Navy were ebbing away with every sentence I wrote.

As I walked back along the King's Road from Brighton westerly to Hove, trying to forget about my miscommunication of classical history in the spring sunshine, MOB, unbeknown to me at the time,, was having difficulties of a very different nature.

"I'm not sure he knew who I was." Eileen said to Bill during mid-morning break that morning.

"In what way?" Bill had also experienced the same, but had been reluctant to impart the knowledge to his mother.

"It was ... when I was talking about the parents' evening tonight, he looked, well, just so distant. When I mentioned the parents that were attending and that we needed to chase up Waldron's father to attend, he said that Waldron wasn't coming back from Messines."

"Messines? But that's in Flanders?"

"He's been doing this more, Bill. He seems to be increasingly ... *back* in the war."

"The night terrors again?"

"Yes, I'm amazed you haven't heard them." The O'Byrnes were occupying the top floor of the Claremont. We had plans to bring in boarders to have some of the rooms but Eileen had held off, saying she wanted the school to 'bed down' first. I had been surprised as I knew how much we desperately needed the income in those first years but trusted her judgement. I didn't find out until much later on from Mick, who returned to a much more lucid state when he left Claremont, just how bad things had got by 1926. He was walking straight up to the pubs by Hove Town Hall and wasn't moving far from them until closing. How he functioned as a headmaster was something of a miracle and now the cracks in the façade were starting to peek through.

"What's he going to be like tonight? He has to give

a speech to the parents." Bill had even investigated using Ralli Hall by the station, so many parents and siblings were attending. This was going to be a big night for the school, and it was all hinged on Mick.

"I don't know," Eileen sighed, "but we need to keep an eye on him."

The parents all assembled in Classroom No. 1 after a welcome drink in the drawing room. Classroom 1 was our go-to room for everything: assemblies, awards presentations, meetings, and, of course, teaching. The stage at the east end of the room was now more substantial and it was on here MOB was to make his address to the Claremont 'family' – the first time all students, staff, siblings and parents were gathered together.

Parents would then meet with staff in the dining room at tables to discuss how their sons had settled in and were performing. Get this right and we had half a dozen more, younger, boys in the bag for the next few years. Get it wrong and parents would pull their boys back to Holland House or elsewhere and Chubb's prediction would be proven correct.

"Ladies and gentlemen, parents, siblings, scholars and non-commissioned officers." Mick cleared his throat. He had a smile at the side of his mouth and was in his element. He had always been where he was most comfortable at Holland House (except for the classroom) when he was addressing parents at a school event. The years fell from him; the gruff exterior that had become his carapace slipped away and the warmth we all knew and saw came to the forefront. He even sounded less Irish.

"Progress," he said, "is a complex term, as how does one measure plates that all spin at different speeds? How do we assess the speed of sailing boats when they can be from different classes, of different sizes, shapes and the wind luffs up our sails, each and every one of us at different times?" He straightened his tie slightly.

"Well, here at Claremont we want to thank each and every one of you for investing your son with us, and we will ensure he makes not just progress, but pays dividends on that investment. How can he not, with such a great assembly of staff, as you see before you? Here at Claremont we provide a friendly home from home, sports as befit a prestigious seaside resort, academic challenge and rigour and most of all … people who care. For if a man entrusts his son to other adults, one needs to know that that man cares about the children as if they were his own."

Mick stepped off the stage and clutched Bill by the shoulder. "I have gone one step further and given my son to the school to teach your children. I don't mind saying, I think he has something of a future here."

Eileen opened the doors. "And now, ladies and gentlemen, we ask you to go with your son to speak to his teachers and myself – in the drawing room and our dining room. They will go over…."

Mick had stopped. The smile had gone. "Over." He just said. His head looked straight forward, but he was looking far beyond the parents gathered in front. I suspected he was a hundred miles away, and eight years ago. I found out I was right.

"Over the..."

"Over..."

"Over the top..."

The room was silent. Mick was not in the room, not really. Not any more.

"It's the ridge. The ridge is the target. It's what we expected."

Eileen walked over to him and squeezed his hand. The whole room was enveloped in white, and painful silence. Nobody spoke, but nobody needed to. They just gaped at Mick O'Byrne, trying to understand just what he was saying, while those of us that knew him and what he'd been through, were working out when he would come back to us. From the trenches.

He slowly, so, so slowly, came back to us and looked Eileen in the eye.

"Is it over?" he said, asking, wishing, pleading.

"Aye, it is." She reassured, not caring that thirty parents and their children were in the room. You knew then, or at least some of us did, that she had done this many, many times before.

Just then Bill strode into the centre of the room.

"Drama!" he interjected. "Drama is where we will guarantee our boys will excel. Isn't that right, headmaster?" Mick nodded, or at least appeared to be nodding.

"Mr O'Byrne is here demonstrating some of the powerful dialogue of our exciting first production; a tale of the fields of Flanders, which we feel every boy should understand, especially whilst the events are still so raw. Claremont is unique as both staff and boys participate in shows. Also, we will not, mark my words, be a school that shies away from the issues of the nineteen twenties. We want every boy to show the power of emotions when he treads the boards. Claremont will encourage all boys to use the stage to develop their public speaking and debating skills – preparing them for the boardroom, the inns of court, the debating society at university and, who knows, even the Houses of Parliament one day."

Bill ushered the parents to the other rooms and I saw the look on his face as he looked at his father when they had left. It was a mix of relief, raw anger and worry combined. I'm not sure which emotion triumphed over the others, but I was bloody glad Bill had been so quick-witted. He was no more a lofty adolescent. This was a confident young man with the baton of leadership firmly in his hands.

It was that night that I first saw him one day running the Claremont, and my prediction would all too soon come true.

MOB continued to deteriorate rapidly that spring. Even his cricket lessons started to be affected; once, when Douggie threw the ball to him, he dived out of its way and cowered on the ground. His temper seemed to grow as his presence in the current day decreased.

One of the boys nearly ended up with a black eye after merely humming in MOB's algebra class. It was clear something would have to be done and Bill and I were increasingly discussing with Ross and Eileen what we could do. It felt as if we were going behind his back, but Eileen had taken him to several doctors and the prognosis was that nothing could be done. For me, a twelve-year-old boy by then, it was particularly strange to be discussing the future of a man decades older than myself. It was even more strange when that man had had such a formative effect on my life, and now I was having a say in his. The words kept cropping up, something must be done. Our worry was that MOB could break down completely and in the process, take all that we had worked for with him.

Our cricketing prowess seemed to be equally dismal. Belmont, our nearest rival school except for Holland House, (but, unlike Holland House, one we seemed to hold genial relations with) constantly beat us at our joint sessions at the cricket ground. The pressure was on – if a school with two huge cricket fans and players couldn't win the odd match then what did that say about our academic prowess?

About that time a strange and rather wonderful notion meandered into my PMM. It seems immature now beyond belief, but it kept nagging away, burying itself deeper and deeper. It was a result of the desperation we felt at MOB's condition.

It was this: what if winning a cricket match despite the odds, could save our headmaster? Could a resounding victory snap him out of his ever-descending spiral into insanity?

It would have to be not just a victory, but a victory

of victories.

That's when it hit me, (and without a book glancing across my cranium this time), the match would have to be one that symbolised the success that we had achieved. Also, our escape from our former dreadful school.

We had to beat Holland House at cricket.

"You did what?"

I had never seen Douggie so angry. We were sat on the beach on a warm Saturday morning in March.

"Bern, he's not in a good way, everyone knows. Losing to Holland will not improve his mental funk one jot. How could you do this?"

"Who says we're going to lose?" I threw a sharp flint at the groyne.

"I do. We all do. The staff do. We can barely hit a ball. Belmont's one-legged player has more runs than most of our team. Christ, Bern, we have a group of schoolgirls who make it their weekly outing to come and laugh at us. The cricket ground reduced our fees as they said we provide so much mirth to the ground staff that they haven't had to increase their wages! How could you be so stupid?"

"We've got until June to get the team into shape. We can do this, Douggie!"

Douggie pointed his finger at me. "One. No, we can't. Two, if we don't, then it'll mean much more than a cricket match – it'll mean Holland is a better school. Three, do you realise how much pressure this'll add to MOB's already addled brow? He's barely getting through the day. Do you really think everyone connected with both schools won't be there? How much do you want to put on his shoulders?"

I stood up and plucked out a small stone that had become embedded in a buttonhole of my jacket. "Well, we'll just have to make sure that we do win." I walked off, leaving Douggie skimming stones into the sea. One hit a gull and I took it as a good omen for our bowling.

As my last ever Sussex summer beckoned and the warm wisps of April sunshine seemed to become an increasingly common feature, I pushed the team harder than we'd ever done before. Bowling, catching, batting, wicket-keeping, you name it, we laboured at it. Cross country now featured me shouting 'change' and we would change direction, as if encountering some invisible stumps.

The boys had to carry their cricket bats to lessons, on runs, everywhere, as if we were a sporting platoon of soldiers, our rifles replaced with willow. In history we studied great games, great batsmen and tactics ventured more and more into maths. We even had a field trip to a local optical lens-making factory so that we could surreptitiously have all the boys' eyes tested.

Our batting average for each of us was slowly getting better; our catching fast and successful. It still didn't feel that victory over Chubb was in the bag, though. I decided to put my engineer's mind to the problem. The solution? Well, it worked, and it may not have been the most traditional of cricket matches, but the following week we had another recurring problem to deal with.

What happened? Well, as the joke goes: how do you keep a right duffer in suspense? I'll tell you later.

My next memory is of my time one morning in the garden at Claremont, sipping a cool glass of dandelion and burdock and reflecting how happy I was that I had secured my scholarship to the school at Herne Bay some months back. I also remember how pleased I was that day that mother was happy for me to lodge with the Paynes as of autumn in their Kent abode. It was June and the days were long. Term was nearing its end and we had nearly made it through the first year at Claremont.

I was helping Bill with some science marking and enjoying the warm scent from the orchids near me that a dotty bee kept strafing. With Herne Bay in the bag, I was letting my other studies slide and focusing more and more on science, which my new school prized heavily. It dominated their lessons and I was determined that their newest recruit wouldn't be a prize flop in that department.

MOB had been much like his old self of late. It seemed that my theory had been right, amazingly; the cricket match had been a mental tonic of sorts. Or so I thought.

A shattering of glass rang out. I heard a shout and ran upstairs.

"It's Ffather." Bill exclaimed, running down the stairs from his classroom towards Room 1. "One of the boys came to fetch me. He's lit a fire!"

"In July?" I asked, but Bill had already run ahead of me into the room. I followed.

Mick was brandishing a poker that had been left in the fireplace, which he had lit some time before, it seemed. The tip was red hot. He had been conducting a science experiment using the effects of heat on metal we later found, but then his mind had tipped into that other place again. He looked frightened and ashamed and the juniors had backed into a corner.

"Out you go, I shouted to them, "Go into the garden." I grabbed Maurice Brigden and whispered, "Get Matron!" in his ear.

Bill slowly walked towards his father. The room was sweltering with the burning coals adding to the June heat. It was clear from the look on MOB's face, he had no idea where he was or who we were. The words he spoke showed his discombobulation; they were nonsensical, distorted and spat out in fear.

"NEED! Two of 'em. Daah! Onners, on I say. ON! We go now, not then. NOW. Targ... Target?"

"Father?" said Bill softly. "Father?"

"Are yer from Seventh company? Where are yer uniforms? How old are yer?" The latter he barked at me.

"Tell me! When's the advance?" His tune had changed now, whatever determination he had had, wherever he was, had gone, replaced by cold fear and calculation.

"We can't go yet – the gunners just don't have the co-ordinates. They don't!" He rushed past us into the hallway, the poker nearly engaging with my eye. I felt its searing heat from its near brush with my head.

"I showed them how to fix bayonets. I did, why didn't they do it in time, the shites?" Tears zigzagged down his face now, changing direction as he shook his head in despair. "Oh the shame, the shame!" His face took on the look of a scared boy and I realised no matter what our age, we all are scared boys when you get far enough underneath.

I tried something. I stuck out my hand towards him, open and palm up. "Mick," I said gently. "It's not a bayonet. You're going to hurt someone, or yourself."

I walked two steps towards him, slowly.

"Will you give it to me please?" I looked deep into his eyes and he looked at me, and then Bill, and then back to me again.

"They shouldn't have let yer join." He said, woefully. "You're just a babe-in-arms. And yer shouldn't be here." To Bill. "Yer don't look strong enough to last." Bill later laughed when he told me the Army enrolment board in 1939 had said much the same thing to him.

"We're not in the trenches." I stated, again, so calmly, although I could feel cold sweat dropping out from under my arms and down my neck. "We're at Claremont and you're home. Safe."

"Safe?" MOB's mood was now wistful. He was somewhere else. "No one is ever truly safe."

"You are." Bill supported.

He started to sing. It was the song that Mick had sung him to sleep with when the roles were reversed and father was looking after son. Eileen told me later that she went through the blues after Bill was born and this great mountain of a man; this rugged mess of a man; this empty shell case whose centre the war had chewed up and swallowed would gently rock Bill over his shoulder, walking up and down their upstairs landing and singing:

Sweet dreams, jellybeans
May your wishes be ice creams.
Life's not always what it seems,
So sweet dream, jelly beans.
Sweet dream, jelly beans,
May you splash in shallow streams.
May your wishes be Peek Freens.
See you when the sun next beams,
Sweet dreams, jellybeans.

Something softened in Mick's features. I stretched my hand out further and stepped again, slowly forward, expecting Mick to ram the poker in my face. Something in his eyes seemed to sparkle and a bit of our Mick came alive again. I wrapped my hand around his and twisted so that I could take the poker out of his grip with my other hand. I mouthed the word 'thank you' as I pulled it slowly away from him, my right-hand half on the poker handle and half on the metal, which even at the handle end was still scorching hot. I stepped sideways and laid the poker on top of the marble radiator next to me.

Just at that point the kitchen had some sort of culinary malfunction. Clouds of steam and smoke started appearing from the door to the basement.

"Gas!" Mick yelled. "GASGASGAS!" He grabbed the lunch bell and started ringing it wildly, shouting at the top of his voice. The staff, students and Buelis the milkman, who had just arrived to collect his money, all found themselves at 11 o'clock stood in the hallway, wondering why the lunch bell was being rung so early.

Mick was suddenly in our world again, his adventure forgotten. "Is it lunch already?" he asked.

Everyone was looking at him, the whole building in silence.

"What is for lunch?" he asked Eileen, who had appeared from the basement. I realised the poker I had laid down had been so hot, still, that it had melted a dent into the marble top of the radiator.

"Beef," she answered. What else?

Later on, with the boys back in class, worried parents pacified, and Mick calmly sat in the drawing room, Eileen called Doctor Soaper, who was the family doctor and had been aware of Mick's condition for some time.

"He needs to go to the Institution," Doctor Soaper said to us in Mick's office. "He can't stay here any more." After hearing what Mick had done, he said: "It can't go on like this."

"But who will run the school?" asked Eileen. "Ross is off to America next week and Bill isn't eighteen until a few months' time."

Doctor Soaper stroked his facial hair. It was bushy

on each side of his face, but he had no beard around his mouth, just mutton chops. He looked like the doctors who served Queen Victoria, I had always thought, recalling a portrait I had once seen. He carried on closing his medical bag.

"I can't tell you the answer to that, I'm afraid, Eileen. But I do know that unless Michael gets some care, the care he needs, like so many of his comrades from the trenches, he won't be around much longer."

Mick however refused the treatment. He was hurt and scornful when all the staff met with him after school that day and said that he had to go. He pulled himself together and moved away, to Hemel Hempstead, as you will recall. He refused to talk to Eileen or Bill and said if Bill ever had kids of his own, he would never have anything to do with them, either. He kept his word.

So the Claremont entered a new era. One with the second of its O'Byrnes as headmaster.

Lesson 15
Graduation

Hove, 1926 and 1940

WOB's first day as headmaster of Claremont was also my last day. I was off to Herne Bay, a few weeks before the end of term for taster days and to meet my new teachers. I wasn't the only one. Ross was off to America the next week – he was leaving also, as he had more golf tournaments to play in America and he believed he could make enough money to settle there now. His investment in the Claremont would remain, though, thankfully, as would the boys, on the whole.

Only one other boy, apart from myself, wouldn't be returning in September and the school wouldn't lose Douggie and the other 12-year olds until Christmas to their new schools. Even better, we had sixteen new boys lined up for the new school year. Mick's erratic behaviour had been tolerated by the parents who had invested their sons in the school. He wasn't the only old soldier in the late twenties having difficulties; hospital wards were still packed with them.

Claremont had made it through its first year of turbulent seas and its new captain was at the helm. Parents were generally pleased that Bill was taking over and the boys were much relieved. Bill was seen as a firm but fair disciplinarian. His age didn't seem to be an issue; he had proved himself to be a dedicated staff and leadership figure. Much of the administration had been managed by him all year anyway as MOB's condition worsened.

As I was about to leave on that Wednesday, Eileen called me upstairs and asked me to check something. I put my bags down, climbed the stairs and walked into Room 1. All the juniors and seniors were there and awarded me a huge round of applause as I walked in.

"Mr James Bernard Clifton." Bill mock-saluted. "It is my pleasure to award you with some gifts in honour of our esteemed thanks for your role in the establishment of this school and to wish you well as our first graduate. For your dedication to the academic side of the Claremont, we award you this fine academic tome to remind you of our numerous lessons of latin!" It was a Latin textbook and the boys had drawn a range of rude illustrations and messages inside.

"Secondly, for your efforts with all other areas of school life, your dedication to recruitment, extra-curricular activities, enterprising methods to help us beat Holland House at cricket (big cheer), and, perhaps most of all, your love of all of the school's offerings at meal times, we award you this, and hope it will always remind you of your brief time here. Wherever you go, however much of a success you become, we look forward to *meet* you again and hope your life will be free of things to *beef* about. Bernard, this is for you."

Eileen wheeled out a trolley and on it was a large

tin of... yes, you guessed it. Covered in icing and marzipan, and with a lit candle for each boy we had managed to recruit. "Boys, off you go!" ordered Bill and the boys all went to form a guard of honour down the front steps.

"And to pipe you out, James laddie," said Ross and ruffled my hair, as Cantaneo and his elderly band stepped into the room from the dining room. The striking chords of Puccini once again reverberated all around the grand Victorian rooms I had come to love so much that year; that had meant so much and had become my first true home since Father had left. I had fought for that building, sweated to make that building a school, a family, and a home and had indeed even slept there, myself, up in a room Eileen O'Byrne had made up on occasions. The violin's calming notes ended and I looked around.

I had been a long way away and a decade and a half back in my mind. I was no longer a schoolboy, but a man of twenty-seven again, a Royal Navy officer and the music I had been listening to in this café here in 1940 had indeed taken me back to those early days of Claremont in the mid 1920s.

I looked around at the hunched figures in the corner of the café. My tea was now stone cold and I dreaded to think what I must have looked like whilst my mind was away, back in the days of my youth.

A young waitress came up to me, brushing down her pinny and smiling. "We wondered what you were thinking about." She confided as she tidied up my teacup and saucer. "We've been placing bets on what you were dreaming about. Mavis here said it was a loved one, but I'm not so sure. I reckon a place, not a person an' all that. I've got a shilling riding on it."

I smiled at her and at Mavis, behind the counter. "Love *and* a place?" I put on my hat. "Well, unfortunately you were both right. It was a place that I loved."

"Rats! I was looking forward to a knees-up tonight on her." She looked peevishly at me. "Does that mean that a good-looking officer like you is ... erm, single then, if I'm not being too forward?"

I smiled very broadly. "You win the money this time. Unfortunately, I have an appointment that I'm going to be late for right now. This evening though ... now, that's a different matter."

Wick Hall was a short walk from the cafe. It had more buildings, more grounds and a more genteel feel than Claremont House. As the school had grown, Bill had needed a larger location from 1933 and this meant he no longer needed to use Ralli Hall near the station and other buildings dispersed over town. It also was a sweet reminder that we had moved in when Holland House moved out, unable to recruit enough students, and they were now defunct.

Clovis Chubb had, apparently, been working for a school in East Sussex before leaving to rejoin his beloved Royal Army Medical Corps again. This time his CO was worried about his mental faculties however, and he was reduced in rank so wasn't doing much more than counting bandages in the quartermaster's store. Old Mother Chubb was now, like MOB in a rest home, where she was, predictably, terrorising the other residents.

I was in agreement with what Mick had said, though, when we'd met last year. I preferred Claremont House too. As proud as I was of the school's success and its expansion, this might be Claremont but not *my* Claremont. Still, I had a promise to keep. Bill had asked me to do a talk, about my projects in the Navy, the ones I was allowed to talk about, to inspire the lads with their science lessons, hopefully. The place may not be the same, but the name was, and so was the headmaster and so I had a duty to perform.

WOB was speaking to the boys in the gymnasium, where they were sat in assembly, as the receptionist walked me in.

"...and so, that is what you need to let your parents know tonight. Letters have gone out. It is simply too dangerous here on the South Coast with a potential invasion from Hitler's troops looking likely if France should fall." He saw me and winked.

"We will be moving to a delightful location in Berkshire, far away from any bombing of London, I hope. Boys, you will have the playing fields, woods and streams to make other boys envious. The rugby, footie and of course cricket we will be able to play, will be endless; the science will be mostly outdoors. We will be able to take everyone who wants to come as a boarder too. I am sure you have questions, yes?"

After answering seven or eight questions, Bill turned to me. Although only barely in his thirties, he looked tired and his temples had grey escapades. He looked like he had bypassed his thirties and was swimming fast through middle age. "Stand up please boys. You've probably been wondering why we have a member of His Majesty's armed forces in today. Well boys, this man is not just a naval officer, but a captain of another sort, too.

"This is Bernard Clifton." I had dropped the James several years before. Bernard seemed to fit my Anglo-Irish heritage far more, and my adopted family whose eldest son was now introducing me. The boys knew who I was and started whispering amongst themselves.

"Lieutenant Clifton, as you need to address him, was once a boy at this school, although at its former location. He wasn't just a boy though, he is also one of our senior partners. But I'll let him tell you all about what he started, and what he's now doing today. Lieutenant Clifton."

I thanked the boys for the applause that followed and the warm welcome from Bill and cleared my throat.

"Good morning, boys. My name is Bernard McCarthy Clifton and I was one of the people who started up this school, which was still called the Claremont School back in 1925, although it used to be in Second Avenue. This happened as I needed a school for my last year before my scholarship and thought I could put one together that was better than my

previous school. That previous school, Holland House Prep, wasn't the best run school in Hove. I would have had to leave anyway as I was eleven and my prep school days were ending, but I walked out just before my twelfth birthday, which was May 30 1925.

I was born in 1913 in 22 Brunswick Place and had to join Holland House as we could no longer afford my previous school. The reason for this was my parents separated in 1925 and the money left just about covered my fees.

I left Holland House because..."

"Where are you off to next?" Bill and I were working our way through bowls of tomato and vegetable soup with brown bread in the school dining room, surrounded by the boys, who were still a friendly,, affable lot. I hadn't realised just how young we all were back at the start. You don't realise what youth truly is until yours is behind you and you never feel as young as you actually were.

The soup was good and much needed; I realised I had hardly eaten a thing all morning. school was doing well despite rationing, but it was certainly not up to Eileen's early days of expensive culinary fare.

I lowered my voice. "Well, after the disaster that Norway's been, I'm involved in pretty hush-hush stuff as the stakes are a lot higher now – French harbours whenever we can."

"Do you think that Jerry will go back to hitting convoys or are our towns going to get it now?"

"I think shipping will always be a target, like the last bash back in 14-18. Adolf's set for wiping our cities out, now Churchill has rebuffed the Fuhrer's offers. Between us Bill, you've definitely made the right move in relocating to Berkshire."

"You reckon?" My old friend, who I had known since I was eleven, grinned and the sixteen-year old I once knew was evident again through his small round glasses. MOB had once said, your age is in your eyes. They tell stories. He was right.

"We've had a breather since Dunkirk, but Hitler's not going to stop now. He's looking for a chance to invade and he needs not only control of the skies over the south, but us all suitably scared."

"Do you think he'll achieve it?"

"Depends on how long the fighter boys hold out. If the airfields take a pounding we'll lose the ability to protect the invasion site, or he may turn his bombers on the cities. Goering can't wait; we all know how much he wants to wipe out London."

"And Brighton and Hove?"

"No doubt in the invasion arena. It's hard to miss on the way to London. The Spanish Armada initially had Sussex as their landing ground, this is just an aerial armada this time. Rumour has it Hitler has the Pavilion earmarked as his holiday home. Get out soon, Bill. The south shouldn't have been used for evacuating children too. This was never going to be a war like 14-18, with Jerry fighting miles away in trenches. This time our trenches will be our beaches, when Adolf comes."

I took a bite of wholemeal bread, aware that food was likely to be sparser as the war dragged on and chewed hard.

"Makes you shudder, thinking of this place in ruins. The piers in pieces, the Grand in rubble. The Metropole torn apart; Pavilion in pieces. We've already got the beaches closed and barbed wire on the front. This never happened last time."

"Funny, its's not those places I think of, nor the people gassed, blown to pieces. I hate the thought of the old Claremont House blown to kingdom come." The place was still my home, all these years later.

"Excuse me? Sir? Mr Clifton? "With all this war going on, do you think a school will ever be set up by a schoolboy again?" A small boy who resembled Douggie was looking up at me. I forgot I was in my twenties and for a moment was a small, very lost, little boy again. I regained my composure.

"What's your name?"

"Telford, Sir. James Alexander Telford. Jatters, they call me."

"Well, Jatters, I'm certain the war will change a lot but we will always have young people who will go on to do great things, so I'm sure anything is possible. It was one thing, though. I was lucky enough to witness and work alongside most certainly a most unique and interesting collection of individuals to run a school. And that includes your headmaster, who himself, once. was very young. You are indeed a most fortunate boy, Mr Telford."

Someone tapped on my shoulder. It was a boy

much younger than Telford. He looked very much like I had done. I wondered if Bill had sat him here for that very reason. There was a theory he had, that there were only one hundred and eighty children in the world and then God started using them up again. I had certainly seen four or five children that I was sure I'd been at school with, despite that being impossible.

"Leff'nant Clefturn, Sir, I just wanted to ask," he wiped a snotty nose on his sleeve, "if it's alright to ask, just, well – what did y' like best when yooo were a' Claremont?"

I looked up, deep in thought. It was that final cricket match. That was us at our best.

I couldn't quite put that in words though, nor did I want to endorse the out-and-out cheating that I had put in place to this impressionable young lad.

Whilst I had been deep in thought, Eileen had whipped away my soup and replaced it with a more predictable dish. She still was trying to make me a carnivore again, bless her.

"Well," I said, "It would simply have to be..." He looked up at me for inspiration.

"The beef."

Fourteen Years Earlier

Hove, 1926

An O'Byrne was speaking, but this was Mick, not Bill. I was wearing cricket whites and the June sunshine beat down on a cricket pitch that years later was due to receive its share of Hitler's bombs in the Second World War.

We were gathered at Sussex County Cricket Ground, the place we had trained at for so many hours, more than the classroom. This was the place we had played match after match and never won one. And now we had to play our nemesis – the school whose pupils and head all hated us. Losing this was more than mere sport – it was the settling of an argument as to which school should carry on and which deserved its spot in this coastal town.

MOB got us all quiet, feeling our nerves. "Right then, lads. I want yer to remember this. Sussex may not claim the birthplace of cricket, we can do stoolball however, but I'm not having you playing a nancy girls' game. Anyway, here in Sussex we were here in the early days and we have the earliest county cricket club in the world – and you're playing on its grounds at its new home. This is the game of a King, my boys, and a King who lived in Brighton. So remember that today, and do us proud. Whatever your background, wherever your birth, cricket is the one great thing on earth."

He wiped his nose on his sleeve.

"Holland House think they're going to beat us, but we've practiced and worked on our skills, speed and teamwork and we have that to beat today. There is no better team I could experience than what we have here. I believe Mr Clifton has a few surprises, too; is that right Clifton?"

I nodded. Over three hundred people were packing out the ground today. The man who rented out cushions, known as 'Cushions' was doing a roaring trade. Every member of staff, student, parent and even Cantaneo and his men were here.

"So let's go and show them what we're made of. Claremont – aye!"

We cheered and ran onto the pitch.

It didn't start well. Chubb's boys were batting with a grudge to settle against the usurpers, the interlopers that we were. Run after run totted up and then it was finally our turn.

We batted well, better than ever, but they were still thirty runs ahead at the first break for tea. Hugill was caught out, then Douggie and then we were left with Parnell-Smith and Howe next. Though bright lads, these two always needed a paperchase to follow any route. When playing rugby, we had to leave lines of paper towards the try line or they'd run around in circles. They had no memory retention of the fact that you had to run backwards and forwards between the stumps, no matter how many times you told them. We had no chance of these two getting any runs. Or did we?

I passed Parnell-Smith the bat I had tampered with. "Look at the top." I said to him.

"It's got a button on the side?" he queried.

"As you run towards the opposite stumps, press it."

"Come again?"

"Just trust me, P.S. Remember, press the button!"

On his first time into bat, he hit a delicious six and ran. Thankfully towards the opposite stumps. This was good. Only anyone close could see that he was dropping a small trail of paper. When he reached the opposite stumps he stopped. The button had opened a small compartment in the bat which had let out a small amount of confetti. Small, but visible enough to any cricketer following it to see it.

"Run, P.S!" I shouted. "Follow the paper!" I mouthed at him. He finally nodded and returned in the right direction. Ninety-six runs later he was finally caught out and Howe took over. The paper trail worked again and Howe clocked out another eighty-four runs. We were now sixteen runs short and there was just me left to bat.

The problem was that bowling against me was Hudson, a huge mountain of a boy. He towered above me at nearly twice my height. Everything about him was hairy: his nostrils, legs, arms and upper lip. It was even said that his tongue was hairy. He looked like he had a permanent growl on his face. Even his eyeballs looked hairy and he had hair sprouting out of his ears at the age of 13. It was rumoured he had hair not only on his palms but on the back of his kneecaps too.

And he detested me. Back in February he had seen me and Douggie in Church Road and we only just missed a severe beating. Hudson wouldn't have stopped with that either; he was known for fighting low and dirty. More than one boy had ended up at Brighton's County Hospital with damage to his tackle due to William Hardwick Hudson. Word was that Chubb recruited him specially after we left Holland House to hand out 'justice' to any Claremontarians he found. He had already broken the cricket box of a boy at Belmont House by aiming deliberately low.

I was in no doubt that he would be aiming for my nether regions, or my teeth and wasn't particularly fussy which. He was also known to be a terrifyingly fast bowler. I gulped as I ran on. The ground went silent. Chubb was the only exception, cheering away from the stands with his high-pitched squeak. He had deliberately lined Hudson up for me; this would be his long-awaited revenge.

As bowlers do, Hudson polished the cricket ball on his whites. Unlike most bowlers though, he delighted on rubbing it on his massive crotch, which reputedly bulged out beneath his school trousers and I remember noticing his flies were broken. I watched as he delighted in rubbing the rouge-coloured ball round and round his gentleman's area. His eyes were locked on mine and he was part-smiling, part-drooling. I felt my own undercarriage shrink in fear. There was no turning back now. I could envisage me never making it to Herne Bay, my face a mash of broken teeth and bones, my family jewels pulped before I had ever had a chance to properly use them.

I clenched the bat and took my position. Hudson sauntered back to the spot from where he would take his run up and achieve his testicular terrorism. He took his time, clearly enjoying the misery he was inflicting in anticipation and the pain he was about to subject me to.

Just as he was about to start his run-up, I heard a noise to the far right of the ground. A large dog was bolting across the turf, aiming straight for the ball. It was Buelis! He was about to attempt his usual trick of stealing the ball to prevent play. A ball that Douggie had managed to wipe with Claremont's trademark tinned beef when the Holland House lot weren't looking during tea.

Hudson had no intention of letting this speeding ugly mutt take his ball. As Buelis launched at the ball, he hid it behind his back with both his hands.

Now, this was a grave mistake. Buelis was not only mad, ugly and demented with a fixation on stealing balls, he also had incredibly poor eyesight and now was unable to determine the difference between the ball behind Hudson's back and the round red stain on the front of the bowler's cricket trousers, both of which smelt of beef. Hudson wasn't the world's cleanest youth either; the red stain had been built up over a number of months. This meant Buelis couldn't discern between a red stain and a red ball. He leapt at great speed and dug his huge teeth around what he thought was the ball he was hoping to bury.

This ball didn't feel like the balls he usually stole, though on this big green, round lawn. It felt squishy and Buelis was amazed as his teeth sunk deep into both sides of this squishy ball. It seemed to be attached to this big boy too, and for some reason this boy was protesting much more than the other boys usually did. His shouting was much more high-pitched and desperate than Buelis was usually used to, so he let go, but not before shaking his head vigorously to have one last go to get this soft, and odd-shaped ball loose.

I only scored a measly twenty-two runs, but Holland House's replacement bowler didn't seem to be concentrating properly for some reason, looking around for other dogs to enter the stadium. He markedly didn't polish his ball anywhere and had taken the unusual procedure for a bowler, of wearing a cricket box for some reason. He wasn't helped by the fact that MOB organised our boys around the ground to bark every time he went to bowl.

As I was finally caught out, we were 8 runs ahead and everyone from Claremont threw their caps in the air. MOB ran onto the pitch and lifted me clear into the air. Bill and the other boys then carried me to the refreshments stall where we celebrated for over two hours.

After endless dancing around the pitch, taunting of Clovis Chubb and squirting each other with fizzy pop, we realised that MOB had been missing for over half an hour. Bill and I suddenly panicked – what if the victory had finally tipped him over the edge? Eileen had no idea where he was either.

Thankfully, a taxi soon pulled up on the edge of the pitch and MOB got out, accompanied by two men. They were from the sports shop in George Street. MOB had cricket pads, bats, stumps and other paraphernalia for each boy. He was animated and effervescent, shouting at the top of his head and grabbing us all, whilst calling for Eileen to get the champagne he'd bought out of the car.

The celebration went on long into the evening, and after which we ended back in the gardens of Claremont with all the parents and we celebrated further still.

"I can't believe we each got a cricket set," said Douggie. "We've wanted the proper gear for so long, rather than wearing cast-offs and patched-together bats."

"Yes," I said. "He's even bought me a cricket box. I think Hudson could have done with this today."

"Do you think you'll still play cricket at Herne Bay?" he asked. "Father will come and watch you if you do." I smiled, thinking ahead to my fantastic future with the Paynes in the next chapter of my life.

"I hope so," I said. "But one thing's certain."

"What's that?" my best friend asked.

"After today, I'm never playing cricket with dogs around."

We laughed and laughed and laughed as we crossed our legs.

The warm June evening was slowly darkening as the waves crashed nearby on the sunny Sussex seashore. It was a night I never wanted to draw to a close.

Epilogue – *1940 and 1987*

Newspaper Report – *The Evening Argus*– 30 September 1940

A TWIN-engine German bomber circled two neighbouring towns yesterday before dropping a stick of four bombs and they fell at the back and front of a well-known boys' prep school in the Brighton area. The principle damage was a large crater in the tennis courts and windows were broken...

...The school was evacuated a few weeks ago and the premises were empty at the time of the bombing...

Bill had got the boys out in the nick of time. Had the school still been there, there would no doubt have been casualties and possibly deaths. I hear the new school at Bradfield College in Berkshire is wonderful. It won't be easy keeping a school going with the war on, but if anyone can, it's Bill, and it will certainly be safer than the south coast. Bill had even reckoned told me the school would be bombed.

"It'll be the blasted Guhl brothers, I bet you," he'd jokingly said to me that day in the Dining Room at St Michael's Hall, which was the other name for Wick Lodge. "Those German boys we took in back in 1926 always had it in for me."

Wick Lodge would be in no state for Claremont to move into when the war ended. What with the bombing and its wartime military occupation, it would have cost a fortune to return to use as a school. I heard by the end of 1944 that Bill was looking for a new venue for the school when the duration was over. The place he had his eye on was Baldslow Place, north of Hastings up the A21. The headmaster there, Arthur Wilson Roberts, was retiring and looking for his school, Langley Place to merge with another.

Yet the cost of the building, was £6,500, way beyond Bill's means after subsidising boys' places throughout the war years and not raising prices to pay for the increasing costs during the war. The least I could do was to make sure Claremont continued in a new home and, let's just say, my wartime inventions meant I had money to spare. Post-war schools would need large grounds and room to grow. The boys were also used to lots of countryside after being in deepest Berkshire – there was no way they could go back to a tiny property or a small garden as we'd had in Second Avenue. The future was for bigger and better schools.

This also meant the days of schools of ten boys were no longer possible and the 1944 Butler Education Act led to the expansion of state, and not private schools. A succession of Labour governments until the 1970s also frowned upon private schools and so it is rare now for a new private school to be set up. When I'd said to my snotty, young friend in Wick Lodge's Dining Room in 1940 that a boy could possibly do what I'd done and start a school, I had been fibbing somewhat. But who knows? As I sit here in the Metropole's bar in Brighton, about to meet a blast from the past who I've been in correspondence with, who has flown over from Australia, a certain Maurice Bridgen – I see that the Claremont is going strong still. It even has plans for an 'O'Byrne Memorial Hall'. Maurice and I have reconnected quite by chance, just because a magazine featured a new hotel due to open this year in 1987 in Second Avenue and that's where we're off to next.

You can probably guess the name of the hotel. Amazingly, and at the same time, Maurice and I both wrote to the hotel, asking if they knew it used to be a school and they put us both in touch with each other. If that can happen against all the odds, then perhaps an eleven-year old boy (or girl) can start up something as amazing as a school. You never know, it might, just might, once more, happen again.

The history behind *Beef*, acknowledgements and further reading

James Bernard Clifton died on September 20 2000 at the age of 87. This story has been pieced together with admiration and fondness for the boy who started a school and then, as a man, went on – not only to play an important role in World War II but also became a fine and important engineer.

James Clifton left behind many inventions that the world has benefitted from, such as the Nanoliter Osmometer you can see online today with his name proudly on it. He produced a power supply for early computers, a transmitter for the Titan II Booster, which was a broadcasting device, although it sounds like a rocket section of the American Intercontinental Balistic Missile and rocket. His genius did even go into space though – the 'inverter' he designed helped lead to the success of the Gemini space programme, the first two-man orbital spaceship.

Earlier in wartime, he also played his part in beating Nazi Germany by designing transmitters for the Royal Navy. Clifton wanted to be known simply as a 'bloody good engineer'. He certainly was that.

It seems unfair and surprising that his name therefore is so little known, and his online profile equally minimal. Thankfully for me, it means his tale has not fully been told before, and only as part of the wonderful book commissioned back in 2003/4 by the Claremont School in its current location, *Pylons and Prefects* by Barbara White (now Veness).

I recommend Barbara's book for those whose appetite for the fuller history of Claremont has been whetted and want to see what happened to the creation of Clifton and the OBs up to the twenty-first century. My thanks to her for all her support and our communications. In the talks I have given on the school, and in my mentions in previous factual books on Sussex it has always caused astonishment that a boy achieved what he did and that it is so little known.

Out of all of Clifton's achievements, however, it is leaving behind this legacy of a thriving school that I think is his most unusual and his greatest. The very famous Summerhill School may have been 'owned' and controlled to an extent by its pupils, who enjoyed a large degree of say in how the school was run, but there are no other examples I have found to date, of schools set up due to the actions of an 11-year old. A slightly wealthy and well-supported 11-year old, admittedly, but still a schoolboy none the less.

Keeping any school going is a huge task and I admire headteachers across the land, past and present, for doing this, but independent schools have the additional stresses of fee-based financing, maintaining often historic buildings and keeping what can be an extended (and often demanding) family intact over the decades. Having the responsibility of running a state school is more like the role of a CEO and education consultant; whereas private school heads are additionally akin, at times, to being the lead figure of a landed family.

From homes to hotels. *Beef Every Day But No Latin* has been due to the wonderful Vicky, Dan and Coralie at the Claremont Hotel, still in the same building that Clifton, nearly a century ago, persuaded MOB and his family to start a school in. They brought to my attention the letters that were written by Clifton in his warm, funny, humble, honest and unique style (he refers to himself as 'the writer'), and also those of Maurice Brigden, whom Clifton had started communicating with in 1986/7.

The rekindling of this friendship (Maurice was indeed one of the younger boys Clifton recruited) seems to have been sparked by the opening of the Claremont Hotel, and its feature in *Australian House Beautiful* magazine, which both spotted, as I mention at the end of the story. This led to them both getting in touch with the hotel to ask if the owners knew it used to be a school, as well as the school in its current location. The hotel decided to put them in touch with each other. Marjorie Clifton, James's second wife (he separated from his first, it seems, due to her love of vodka) also wrote to the school back in 2001 nine years before her death in 2010 and it is these letters that also helped the basis of my research.

Peter Beaumont and his staff at the school today

very kindly allowed me access to their archive material once and the wonderful Keep in Falmer, the record office of Brighton and East Sussex helped me discover more about Hove at this time. I hope Hovians don't mind this Brightonian invading over into their territory and Brightonians don't mind me neglecting the big, brash brother of the siblings that make up this fantastic city, (as it has been since 2000). My thanks also to the staff at Worthing's wonderful Local Studies Section of the Library and Information Centre, who helped me track down the custodian of Claremont School's history, Barbara Veness.

Clifton's life in these early days just seemed to be told better from his mouth, and so I have tried to let him speak here, rather than describe the actions and events in a history book. Where there are gaps in information about these characters who made the school what it was in its early days, it has been left to me to attempt to plug these gaps and flesh out these characters. I hope I have been successful. MOB, Clifton, Douglas Payne and all the others have been dominating space in both my heart and 'PMM' for the last two years and, almost like a medium, I have tried to be the vehicle to let them speak across the decades to us here today in the twenty-first century. They seem real to me in many ways, and so I hope, where I have inferred the conversations they needed to have in the creation of the school and its running in its early years, they are as true as private conversations this author wasn't privy to can be.

Beef is a work of historical fiction therefore as

closely woven to historical fact as possible, (the individuals and the events they are involved in) as I could make it. The Claremont School has no records surviving from its early days (nor are there likely to be, with the unfortunate MOB's deteriorating state of mind in the mid-1920s) and so I have had to attempt to join together jigsaw pieces of the past and provide my own interpretation where this was necessary. If any further information ever comes to light, I would of course be keen to hear about it – please contact info@allinclusivehistory.org or call 07504 863867.

Any mistakes made of course in the writing of this book, are wholly mine and I would always welcome equally any feedback. I would also like to hear about more inspirational young people from the past as I think it is important young people of today remain inspired from the past and realise that some of the old people they see on the streets, in shops and cafes, once were young, too, and capable of great things.

MOB's time as headmaster, his alcoholism and long-term effects from World War I are true, the latter, sadly – he did really ring the bell for lunch when befuddled and Bill did have to take over the headship at such a young age. Bill didn't take over until 1928 in real life however, and so I have cheated with chronology and placed the event in 1926 so that Clifton could be there too, whereas in reality he had been at Herne Bay School for two years by that time.

MOB must have made some sort of recovery, or at least spent many years surviving his traumatic war recollections, as he survived long past 1928 but his later years are something of a mystery. Why Clifton moved in that year from Sussex over to the 'Far East' of Kent seems to be because Douglas Payne's father, Austin Bowen Payne (who really was a famous cartoonist for the *Mirror*), lived there, so it made sense that the Paynes would, at some point, probably relocate to have just one seaside house. Payne's brother was the even more famous G. M. Payne, who drew the very famous 'Brown Family War Christmas' cartoon that GCSE students of World War I will know well. It is a shame we don't have any correspondence or records from that time from Douglas Payne. He seems a much-needed and supportive part of Clifton's life.

From 1926 onwards, WOB was left to run the school without Clifton, but Eileen would help out, running the school in its different locations until after MOB's wife's death in 1959. Bill's wife, Jean (nee Dalrymple) would also be a mother to the school and its boys until her death from cancer in 1963. MOB was definitely out of the picture from 1928 after some sort of row, which I have tried to surmise in the book, and would have no contact with his grandchildren that WOB would later have with his wife Jean.

Jean at the school's fourth home of Baldslow Place carried on the tradition of female O'Byrnes as matrons and by that time had a team of four staff. MOB, like Alec Ross, lived until 1951 so, as I implied earlier, must have either made some sort of recovery or had a supernatural liver. Clifton met with him twice in 1939 (and filmed both visits), but for convenience I've focussed on just one visit. Both films, and the cricket gear MOB gave Clifton and the rest of the team after their one and only win in cricket apparently didn't survive World War II but would be wonderful to see. All we have is a few pictures of MOB, who looks remarkably like Ross (Ross, as Clifton mentions, has a wonderful habit of looking to his right in any photo as if he has spotted something more interesting than the photographer. The exception is one photo, the one in the garden of Second Avenue, where he is still avoiding the direct glare of the camera, but looking this time the other way!

Ross is the biggest mystery – I had little to go on with this key individual who not only helped co-fund the start-up of Claremont, but was one of its earliest staff. He also seems to disappear from view about the same time as Clifton, so I had him heading off to America as James departed. Apart from photos and being described as 'Ross, a golfer', the only mention of him is a street directory, where he is jointly listed with MOB and named as 'A. A. Ross'. This is as much as I could find; he doesn't appear in the 1911, 1921 or 1931 censuses for Brighton and Hove. Despite being a 'golfer', there is no evidence of which golf clubs he played at here in Sussex, and my thanks to Barry Hughes, Hon. Membership Secretary, Brighton and Hove Heritage Commission for his investigations here.

The only 'Ross, A.' who appears to be a golfer at this time is Alec Ross, the famous golfer at this time who seems to have been in America by this stage, and whose brother is the famous Donald J Ross, designer of 400 American golf courses, and himself a one-time international player. My thanks to M. J. Fay at the Donald J. Ross Society in the USA for their correspondence. Our Ross doesn't seem likely to be this Ross (although it did make me wonder if he was an inspiration for the golf-mad Trump family of today, and whether his name inspired the naming of a certain Donald J. Trump – there are no other Donalds in his family I could find).

Another Ross sibling with the initial of A (for Aneas) was rumoured to be the village drunk back in the family village of Dornoch in Scotland by the mid-20s, so it sounds unlikely to have been him. Alec Ross by this time apparently wasn't making enough money in the USA to travel back to Britain, let alone have any reason to visit Sussex. After toying with several options, I have decided to take the romantic option and assert that our A. A. Ross was Alec Ross and he did somehow make it to Sussex and became entangled with James' mother.

If the school could include a Hollywood star in its staff, then it could be possible that it attracted an international golfer playing tournaments, still, around the world in the 1920s. If it was Alec Ross, he died the same year as MOB in 1951. I would be keen to hear otherwise.

Talking of deaths, running the school from his late teens - only seven years on from Clifton's age - combined with the stress of keeping the school going through the difficult war years, and in the years of austerity afterwards, almost certainly contributed to Bill's continuous ill-health. It may also have led to his very premature death, at the age of only 43, in 1951. It probably killed off not only Bill, but his promising cricketing career too. Claremont was his father's final project at the end of his career, but to Bill, it would be his entire working life and only job. It is justly fitting that the O'Byrne theatre at Claremont School today at Baldslow Place is so named. Early pupils have said the school would never have got started without Clifton, but it is WOB who ensured the school kept going and is still going today. His early death seems the price he paid for that, and the life and times of WOB and the school he led are surely worthy of a Sunday night drama.

Independent schools have lives of their own, with traditions, drama, passion, excitement and intrigue able to rival any Downton Abbey or Poldark. Like any school, they are a family, but with the pressure of maintaining a usually historic and extensive house and grounds as well as looking after that family. The descendants of WOB and MOB are alive and kicking today, but Jeremy O'Byrne, Bill's son and his sister sadly ended up leaving their home when the headmastership was offered elsewhere.

The departure of the final O'Byrnes from the Claremont was somewhat acrimonious, as Jeremy admits today, but it was good to hear that both he and his wonderful wife were welcomed back to the school on visits in the last few years. They too made me very welcome on an afternoon visit to their Sussex home and my thanks for both that and their generous help in piecing together more of the jigsaw. I hope you both like the end result and it is an honour to know even two members of your wonderfully fascinating family.

MOB arriving injured in Brighton after Passchendaele is my invention but is as good an explanation as any (with Brighton being a hospital town during the Great War) as to why this Irish family which had lived in Orpington and Plumstead in London ended up in Brighton and Hove in the 1920s. There is no evidence, either, about Ross being Estelle Clifton's lover, but I felt that there needed to be an invented reason for his involvement with Claremont and his willingness to co-fund the school.

The caning scene is pure invention but from Clifton's huge disdain for his old school, I surmised that the wonderfully-named Clovis Chubb had presented the boy with reason for the disdain and it is not implausible that Chubb's reaction to this very unusual situation would have been so extreme. Chubb was also hated by many boys who left Holland House because of his sadistic nature and vigorous canings, so such a reaction by him seems likely.

Herbert Marshall was indeed a future Hollywood star, who briefly worked for the school as its swimming teacher and did indeed teach one-legged breast stroke. King George V was also, apparently unable to tell correctly which was his fake leg. The story that it was Chubb who cost him his leg was pure invention but adds to the villainy of the pantomime villain of our story. If *Beef* is nothing else, it is indeed the acknowledgement of a gathering together of a wonderful collection of unique and semi-prominent human beings, each of whom deserves their own biography and national prominence. There are a lot of people throughout time that we have collectively forgotten as a nation and, as we approach the centenary of this era, perhaps we should look at another 'twenties' that was as difficult an era, but in a different way to our own decade.

There really was a match that made MOB so excited he bought cricket pads and bats for the boys, or at least for Clifton. I took the liberty of making it against Holland House, and inventing Clifton's enterprising methods of helping the victory come about. Holland House did indeed seem to close down soon after Claremont made its first move and did indeed take in Clifton's 'enemy' before that stage, the fairer sex. I have no idea if losing a cricket match caused this closure though, but it is at least a metaphor for Claremont winning the battle for survival over its rival.

One event I have discovered no proof for but have added, as I strongly feel it could have been the case, was Clifton providing the huge sum of £6,500 for WOB to purchase Baldslow Place after the war so that the Claremont could continue in a new home after Berkshire. Correspondence at the time says that the school had lost money throughout the war and the O'Byrnes were not in a position to fund the purchase themselves. Purchasing Baldslow would either have required a hefty loan, which there is no record of, or an alumnus must have donated some money. With Clifton's presumably inherited wealth by that time, his links and his highly successful work from the war, it seems likely that he was the donor and therefore not only the school's founding partner, but its financial saviour as it re-established itself anew.

That he would want to see the school he had got going, keep going, is a logical premise and one I've stuck to here. It meant that the Claremont School was under ownership of the O'Byrnes until the death of Jean O'Byrne, Bill's wife, in 1958. This was not before she, too, had taken her turn and led the school, but this time jointly with her brother – the first non-O'Byrne headmaster. When visiting today you will see the chapel at today's Claremont at Baldslow was rightly refurbished in Bill's honour and Jean has also a memorial area still at the school, both of which are richly deserved.

Beef seems very much a book we needed when I started researching and writing it, with schools becoming increasingly pressurised exams factories over the last two decades and a lot of the fun, characters and excitement of working and learning in schools being lost. I hope that it is now a needed diversion from our own current problems in the 2020s and shows us how people dealt with their problems back then. Claremont was certainly a collection of the most unusual characters, some of whom were dealing with 1920s problems – their personal consequences of fighting in the First World War.

This is also a reason why I think this book is

needed: we study the political, economic and international consequences of the war, but have neglected the social consequences. One book that does cover the testimonies of those who faced the post-war era admirably is *The Road Home*, by Max Arthur. My own family on my mother's side at this time in Brighton were dealing with a father who had died, aged 33 in 1920 from his gassing in the trenches, so my grandfather, Arthur Bartlett, would never know his father. James Bernard McCarthy Clifton put the Claremont School together partly because he wanted to create a school, but also to create in its new headteacher of MOB the father figure he so badly needed.

Good schools can make a difference still today and can sometimes help replace the holes children have in their lives. The hole in the fictional Harry Potter's life from the death of his parents is partially filled by the strength he draws from Hogwarts, and Claremont did the same for Clifton to some extent. MOB may have been a Gene Hunt-style mentor, but he was needed at that time by Clifton. Subsequently, Clifton's experience at Claremont of starting and helping run a school seems to have supercharged him and inspired him to lead the full and significant life he did. Perhaps also the love and warmth he received from his new, created family also helped make him the success he became throughout his long life. I hope, truly, it also gave him the love he hinted that was missing as he approached his adolescence.

The fun, and excitement, and pride and team

feeling of the Claremont School in the 1920s that comes across should also remind us that schools are primarily about children, not just the results they achieve at exams. We have forgotten along the way through our centuries of educating children what is possible when adults and children truly work together and, most of all, that in this life, our children are what matters most.

In the post-COVID 19 world, our children will have lost a huge chunk of their school life and perhaps this is the time to build small, friendly schools with the warmth and humour that Claremont had.

Kevin Newman, Sussex, 30 July 2020.

Further Reading

Pylons and Prefects – Barbara White (Now Veness) – published by Claremont School, 2004

The Encyclopaedia of Hove & Portslade, various volumes – Judy Middleton (2003)

The Road Home, Max Arthur (Phoenix, 2003)

The Claremont Guest House

The Claremont Hotel, where the Claremont School was first based is today a wonderful 5-star boutique guest house which also hosts a range of artistic and lively events, run by a very friendly and welcoming family. Interestingly, the children there still play a leading role and when I first held a book launch there, they had all us adults well under control! The spirit of James Clifton must have been embodied in the Victorian walls of the house and is still alive today.

Claremont House, that the guest house is based in, is also the only property in Second Avenue that has not been subdivided so, from an architectural aspect, it is definitely of interest and an excellent example of a Willett's-made property. Should you wish to visit the hotel for a cream tea, meal or to stay, contact info@theclaremont.eu or call 44 (0)1273 735161. Their website is www.theclaremont.eu/

Walking, motorised tours and other books by Kevin Newman

All-Inclusive History runs a range of talks and walking and motorised tours of Sussex, including a *Beef Every Day But No Latin* walking tour of Hove and talk on this book. For further details of these, and of Kevin's other books please call 07504 863867 or email info@allinclusivehistory.org

©2020 Kevin Newman

CHRISTMAS 1925
J. CLIFTON
J. HUGILL
B. TURLE
D. PAYNE

LENT 1926
A. CHAMIER
R. SHERRIFF
N. SHERRIFF
R. SIMMONS
E. HALL
M. BRIGDEN

SUMMER 1926
G. RICHARDSON
M. PARNELL-SMITH
G. WALDRON

The Real Press

If you enjoyed this book, take a look at the other books we have on our list at
www.therealpress.co.uk

Including the new Armada novel with a difference, *Tearagh't*, by the maverick psychologist Craig Newnes.

Or the medieval thriller *Regicide*, by David Boyle, and introducing Peter Abelard as the great detective...

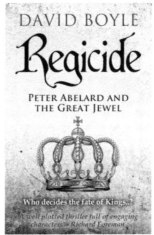

Printed in Great Britain
by Amazon